Bodybuilding Meal Prep Cookbook

Bodybuilding Meal Prep Recipes and Nutrition Guide with 2 Weeks Dieting Plan for Men and Women. Get Your Best Body Ever!

Eric Hockman

Disclaimer

The recipes and information in this book are provided for educational purposes only. Please always consult a licensed professional before making changes to your lifestyle or diet. The author and publisher shall have neither liability nor responsibility to anyone with respect to any loss or damage caused or alleged to be caused directly or indirectly by the information contained in this book. All trademarks and brands within this book are for clarifying purposes only and are owned by the owners themselves, not affiliated with this document.

Images from shutterstock.com

CONTENTS

INTRODUCTION

What can be as essential for bodybuilding as workouts are? The secret is simple – it is a well-balanced diet based on your individual needs. It might be tough to follow any diet, especially if you aren't used to a healthy lifestyle. There are a lot of seductions and temptations that can take you right off the road, and when that happens you feel bad about yourself. Forget about failures and self-destructions! Our cookbook is your salvation. Open the science of meal prep – the world of possibilities that will help you to make your way to perfect and healthy body much more easily.

We will show you how to use all the advantages of meal prep for bodybuilding goals. A lot of useful information and advice are waiting for you. Where should you start? What should you eat to gain weight? How can you benefit from it? You will find all answers in our book! Here is your game-changer! Ready, steady, go!

What is Meal Prep?

Do you ever feel tired of wasting your time in the kitchen every day? Sometimes you may think it isn't worth it, but you still want to eat something. It's especially hard after a long training session in the gym and after work. If you want to change something in your cooking routine, congratulations! You have found the solution! Meal prep is an excellent way to make your life much easier than ever before.

The main reason why you should take a look at meal prep is that it allows you to be more flexible in your cooking preparation: you can cook a certain number of portions in the meal prep box and store it in the fridge until you need it the next day or even three days later.

But more words are needed to describe what meal prep is. Your daily routine becomes an interesting process of creating your own diet plan where you are the chef and nutritionist.

Who knows what restaurant food or semi-finished products are made from. Now the quality of your ingredients and meals depends only on you.

Start your own cooking expertise to make your food a more effective source of necessary nutrition, experiment with different variations of the ingredients until you find perfect combinations for your life-style. Feel free to share your plans and new meal prep ideas with the Internet community!

The Main Advantages of Meal Preparation

✓ **No more harm**

Every day we waste money on nearby fast-food or snacks, being seduced by our hunger. It's not only harmful to us but for our diet too. Meal prep will be a guard of your new lifestyle. Just cook some healthy snacks that fit in with your diet, and then you will never again fall into the trap. Next time you hear that rumbling in your belly, it doesn't matter if you are in the office or at home, grab your snacks from the fridge and stay fit. Don't let the hunger hit you!

✓ **You are the control group**

When you cook the meals, there's no mystery about what it has been made of. You control everything from the cleanliness of your kitchen to the nutrition of every ingredient. You also control how fresh the products are and you can decide which way is better to cook them. You become the creator of the powerful weapon that will make your body stronger and healthier.

✓ **No more overeating**

With meal prep, you will never stay hungry for long. Forget about slobbering while cooking or waiting for delivery boxes; just heat your glass container full of a cooked homemade meal. You don't need to find a new source of food. Thanks to meal prep, you won't overeat when you finally sit down for a meal because you won't be as insanely famished.

✓ **Save your time**

When you cook all your dishes for the week at the weekend or just pre-cook all of the ingredients, after a long hard day, you will say 'thank you' to you from the past. You can enjoy a tasty ready dinner and you don't have to cook, go to the store, or order delivery. Meal prep not only saves you time but allows you to spend it doing something you need to do or like. For example, have a rest or a good training session, hang out with your friends, or other activities.

✓ **Save your money**

Total control also means that you control the cost of your dishes. Try to find the benefits and create meal prep plans based on sales in your grocery store. You can be sure that meal prep helps to avoid waste of money and products, saving you from an unnecessarily stuffed grocery basket or ordering every lunch and dinner out.

✓ **Release yourself from stress**

You can't deny that dieting, cutting calories, especially with exhausting training in the gym, can make you think about food all day long. You feel like all your willpower is drained too fast, and you almost give up and want to go off your plan. You're so tired and not in the mood to make the right choices. You will be amazed how meal prep can motivate you not to give up and releases your mental stress. You will feel much better after following the meal prep plan, and your goals will be reached more easily.

Why Meal Prep is good for Bodybuilding

Bodybuilding meal prep is a part of creating the body of your dreams. Without establishing a solid diet plan, all your efforts in the gym become a waste of time and health. As a bodybuilder you need the right nutrients to gain strength. A good diet plan will increase your well-being and motivation to continue your hard work.

How meal prep improves workouts?

You won't achieve your goals without following a well-balanced diet. Of course, it will be stressful for you as for beginner, especially if you aren't used to eating healthily. A strict diet such as keto, paleo, or high-protein diet will feel like a punishment in the beginning. The stress comes with food restrictions, but you won't be tempted to break your diet if you have prepared nutrition-packed meals beforehand.

The main idea of meal prep is that the person has total control of the food ingredients, portion sizes, and amount for the whole week. You can decide if you need to adjust the lean protein for your strength training. Knowing how the meals have been made, you can be sure that you get all of the essential nutrition for your workout routines.

✓ **At first, set priorities**

Calorie intake is a necessity for building muscle mass. A person needs to eat more calories to build muscle than the body burns every day. The general recommendation is to increase the number of calories by 15-20%. This means you should add more lean protein like egg whites and grass-fed beef or protein shakes to the daily meal plan to increase your protein intake.

✓ **Start your day with muscle-building breakfast**

Breakfast is the most important meal of the day to give us energy for our activities and bodybuilders know how to gain the maximum benefit from breakfast. The first meal of the day has a variety of options for bodybuilding needs. The most popular choice is oatmeal, skim milk, and eggs. Also, you can add a smoothie bowl that is filled with energy-rich grains and fruit to your bodybuilding breakfast meal prep. Consider peanut butter, chia seeds and berries for fiber and protein.

✓ **Add more calories to your lunch**

A good mix of protein and calories is a healthy lunch for bodybuilders. Lunchtime probably catches you while you're working at the office or somewhere else and have no possibility to eat according to your meal plan. Meal prep is your insurance for following your meal plan at any time, and it doesn't matter where you are. Try to roast some vegetables with olive oil which goes perfectly with salmon. Sliced ham with your choice of salad or fruit is a good choice too. Roasted Brussel sprouts, chickpea salad, or a kale salad with nuts and corn are the best alternative for vegetarians.

✓ Time for after-workout dinner

You need to get an equal amount of vegetables, protein, and carbs for your dinner. The best options are quinoa, pasta, buckwheat, and sweet potatoes because they rich in carbohydrates. Also, don't forget to eat protein-rich foods like fish, chicken, turkey, and beef or pork.

✓ Protein Needed for Each Meal

Being a bodybuilder, you need to think about how to optimize your daily protein needs. It's important to know how much protein you need for each individual meal. You should understand that every person has nutritional needs that vary based on her/his size, age, and caloric needs. Nutritionists or fitness trainers can help with determining your nutritional needs. Remember that building muscle mass doesn't mean a person needs a ton of protein.

Meal prep will be effective only with the right nutrition.

✓ A glass of protein shakes

A protein shake is good solution to get your protein needs. Try them before or after a workout.

Of course, the best way you can get protein is from your usual meals, but because of a lack of time, a serving of protein shake might be the only option. Protein helps your body to repair torn muscle fibers from grueling and exhausting workouts. The modern market offers a lot of types of protein powders, so look for those that suit your body best.

✓ Try to avoid processed foods

There are a lot of products in the grocery store, and the majority are processed foods. Today it's hard to find something natural because of added preservatives, sugar, and salt . Some of them are dangerous for our bodies. Unfortunately, we can't get by on only processed foods, if there is the possibility of buying fresh whole foods, go for it. Food in its original state is rich in nutrients, and nothing else can replace it.

✓ Smart Carbs

Hunger is the permanent companion of bodybuilding and dieting. So, it means you need to eat types of food that will keep you full for longer and will give you energy for your workouts. The best options for this are sweet potatoes or oatmeal because of their richness in moderate glycemic carbohydrates. Such forms of carbohydrates do not break down quickly, ensuring that they do not instantly turn into blood sugar. Complex carbohydrates give you the energy you need without additional saturated fat and sugar.

✓ **Stay hydrated**

Remember feeling and biting dry lips? You may think it's normal but it's not, especially if you are working on your bodybuilding goals. We often forget how important hydration is. Lack of proper hydration will delay great workout progress. Dehydration reduces performance and muscle building becomes ineffective. Your strength will decrease, and you will feel how tough your workouts are. That's how necessary hydration is, so always remember to drink more water during the day.

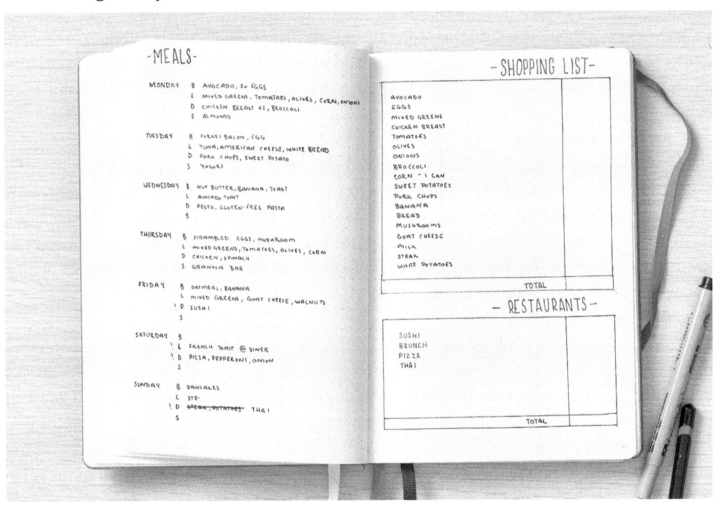

How to Create Your Meal Plan

What is your first thought about meal prep? Probably, you aren't impressed and might even terrified of the idea that you need to spend all your Sunday in the kitchen, cooking a lot of food. Or, maybe, you don't want your meals to be bland and unfresh after being in the fridge for the whole week. For sure, all of those reasons are stereotypes. No, we aren't saying it cannot happen, but it is the result of thoughtless planning.

Of course, you can't create an ideal plan at once without any experience, and if you are serious about packing on muscle, losing weight, or just adding more healthy food to your life, you need to get to know the meal prep science. So how can you get started?

✓ **Start a journal**

You will notice that a little notebook makes the process of creating meal prep plans much easier. Write down all your requirements, graphics, workouts, and a weekly meal plan. Don't forget about the grocery list! Systematize your thoughts, and you will see the clear picture in front of your eyes. The journal minimizes the risks that you will make a mistake or forget something. So, let it be the key to a healthy and perfect body.

✓ **Cook simple meals**

Diversity is the main feature of the culinary world, but for meal prep, you need to concentrate on other features. Meals must be simple and ready to use when you need it. Take proteins, veggies, and starches as essential ingredients for your dishes. Then, when you figure out what works best for you, use your culinary skills to add some gourmet notes. The more experience and skills you have, the more possibilities that are open to you, so don't be afraid of to experiment.

✓ **Make a grocery list**

Don't go shopping without a grocery list. It's called a 'newbie mistake'. Without it, you can be seduced by things you don't need. Sit and think rationally, don't hurry. This list will show how much money and products you need for your meal prep plan. Write it down and then check if you can save some money or maybe you wrote down some excess products. Also, you can keep your grocery list for future shopping. Believe us, and it will save not only your money but even your time walking around the store.

✓ **Size and structure matter**

Try to chop your ingredients in the same sized pieces to cook them evenly. Also remember that some vegetables will be ready earlier than others because of their structure. So, it's better to cook them separately or add them in at a different time. If you don't, then one-half of the veggies will start to burn, while the other half isn't ready yet.

✓ **Frozen may help**

The freshness of products is the biggest secret for all customers. So maybe we should give frozen products a chance. Fruits and vegetables are frozen right away after being picked. They probably have more nutrition than their fresh alternatives in the grocery store. Who knows how long they have been lying there? It's better to make a frozen mixture on your own. Find a reliable source of fresh veggies and fruits, and combine your favorite ones, place into an air-tight freezer bag, and leave in the freezer until you need it. It's preparations for your next meal prep! Sounds lovely, doesn't it?

✓ **Fridge or freezer?**

Meal prep has several options for storing food. Keep it in the fridge or freezer it until you need it. Freezing doesn't affect the texture or taste in most cases, but we recommend you store your cooked meals in the refrigerator. Why? Some products such as potatoes, leafy greens, and zucchini don't rejuvenate after freezing. Next, just reheat your cooked dish and enjoy it!

How to store meal prep

You should always know how long your meals will be safe in the fridge. In general, it is safe for three to four days. A good tip is using erasable markers. Have you ever seen restaurant food storage? Each container has the information about when it arrived or was prepared. Using different markers will help you not to forget on what day of the diet you should eat each meal and how long it can stay in the fridge. Remember! You can place your meal prep food in the fridge only when it's completely cooled down.

Don't be afraid to fail because we are all learning. You don't need to create amazing bento boxes or professional recipes. The more you cook, the more you improve your skills. So, have fun trying new methods and recipes!

The role of Nutrition

Nobody can deny the importance of proper nutrition for our body. Now we will explore the basics of nutrition. You will see what types of food should be in your diet. A well-balanced diet is a base for good health and a perfect body.

The Major Nutrients

Nutrition is an essential thing for the survival and development of all creatures. Nutrients are food components that provide nourishment, so we can survive. They give us energy, help maintain and build body tissues, bones, organs, teeth, and are responsible for regulating body functions such as metabolism and blood pressure. Nutrients are protein, fats, carbohydrates, vitamins, minerals.

Protein

Protein is the necessary building blocks that our body uses for proper function. It participates in building and repairing our body tissues, such as skin, muscles, and organs. You can find protein in meat, poultry, fish, eggs, cheese, milk, nuts, dried beans, peas, and soy products. Our bodies can also convert it into fat or use it as a source of energy. The amount of protein needed is individual for each person because it depends on body size, age, activity level, and well-being. Sick and undernourished people need a higher amount of protein to help their bodies maintain the regeneration processes.

Protein sources:

Poultry	turkey, chicken
Fish	salmon, tuna, cod, trout, bass
Beef	steak, ground beef, hamburgers, stew meat, hot dogs
Shellfish	shrimp, lobster, crab
Milk	cow milk, milk products
Eggs	white egg
Soy products	tofu, tempeh, veggie burgers
Legumes	white beans, chickpeas, kidney beans
Peas	green peas
Nuts	almonds, pistachios, walnuts, cashews, peanuts
Seeds	pumpkin, sunflower, squash seeds
Butter	peanut butter, rest nut butter

Carbohydrates

Carbohydrates are the main resource of energy for our bodies. Without it, we can't function effectively. Carbohydrates enrich our body with starch, sugar, and fiber. You can find starches in potatoes, grains, beans, and peas. Sugars can be found in fruits, vegetables, and sweeteners. Whole-grain foods such as bread, cereals, fruits, and vegetables are rich in fiber. Fiber's importance is hard to estimate: it helps digestion, lowers cholesterol, helps to feel fuller for a longer time. Without it, there can be problems with the bowel.

Carbohydrates sources:

- grains
- bread of all kinds
- potatoes
- beans
- peas
- oatmeal, muesli
- rice (white, wild, brown)
- breakfast cereals
- tortillas
- grits
- pasta, noodles
- popcorn
- quinoa
- crackers (all kinds)

Fats

The next essential nutrient in our diet is fat. There a lot of stereotypes that fats are bad for us, but this isn't true. We need it for the protection of our body and organs, for normal functioning of the membranes in the cells in our body, and for nerve and brain function. It is also used to insulate the body and prevent heat loss. Excess fat may also be used for body energy or retained.

Even though you need fat in your diet, remember that you are not able to eat too much fat. A diet high in fat often leads to serious and harmful complications such as high cholesterol, heart attack, coronary artery disease, or cerebrovascular accidents. So be careful! Products that contain fat are oils, butter, margarine, salad dressings, meat, fish, milk (animal fats).

Some fats are healthier than others. For example, eating a handful of nuts is a better choice than eating a handful of potato chips. There are three main types of fats: polyunsaturated fats, monounsaturated fats, and saturated fats. Polyunsaturated can be found in corn, safflower, soy, sunflower oil, and omega-3-fatty acids. Monounsaturated fats can be found in vegetable fats such as olive oil and canola oil. Saturated fats can be found in butter, lard, bacon, coconut oil, and peanut oil. Saturated fats are less healthy than other fats. You need to limit their quantities.

Fat sources:

- oils
- butter
- milk
- eggs
- fish

- meat
- nuts and seeds
- avocados
- margarine
- salad dressings

- olives
- peanut butter
- animal fats found in meat

Vitamins

Vitamins are essential to help our body to ingest the other nutrients we take in, and they also participate in the process of tissue growth. If you're following a well-balanced diet, then you do not need to take vitamin supplements, while other people may need to intake a daily supplement as a necessity for their body needs. We need the following vitamins everyday:

Vitamin A is responsible for the good condition of the skin and supports eye health. The source of vitamin A is dark green, yellow, and orange vegetables.

Vitamin B is necessary for the normal functioning of the digestive and nervous systems. It is important for digestive carbohydrates, protein, and fat. Metabolism is the process by which the body converts what we drink and eat into energy. Vitamin B can be found in such products as meat, milk products, green leafy veggies, and fortified grain products.

Vitamin C strengthens blood vessel walls and participates in the regeneration of wounds and bones. The other function is absorbing iron. Citruses such as oranges and grapefruit, strawberries, brussel sprouts, broccoli, and green cabbage can enrich our body with vitamin C.

Vitamin D is one of the base elements for building bones and teeth. It can be found in fortified orange juice, butter, milk, salmon, tuna, sardines, and liver.

Vitamin E is an essential antioxidant, which is used to remove damaging free radicals. Vitamin E assists the immune system to work properly. The main sources are fish, nuts, wheat germ, vegetables, fruits, and cereals.

Minerals

For the best function of our body, we need to intake minerals. Minerals are compounds that are required by our body to perform a huge amount of functions. They are an essential part of any well-balanced diet.

Potassium is responsible for normal heart function, contracting of muscles, and for effective nerve conduction. Products that are rich in potassium are yogurt, squash, potatoes, tomatoes, dried apricots, and bananas.

Calcium is needed for strong bones and teeth, proper muscle contraction, blood clotting, and proper heart function. The best sources for calcium are yogurt, ice cream, cheese, leafy green vegetables, and canned fish, such as sardines.

Iron participates in the creation of hemoglobin, part of red blood cells. You can find it in red meat, chicken, pork, dark green leafy veggies, iron-fortified cereals, grain products, and dried fruits.

Sodium helps to maintain fluid balance. Most processed food includes sodium, for example, meats and soups, olives, pickles, packaged mixes, and vegetables. The amount of sodium should be limited in your diet.

Iodine is needed for normal thyroid gland functioning. It is important for our metabolism. It can be found in fish such as cod, canned tuna, shrimp, iodized table salt, milk, and yogurt.

Water

Water is important to all life, human life included. We cannot survive without it. We need water for elimination, digestion, and control of body temperature. Every day we need to drink about 8 glasses to stay hydrated. Liquids such as coffee, tea, juices, milk, and soda can also provide us with fluid. Anyway, it's better to drink water, milk, and juices. Remember to stay hydrated!

Eat, Buy, Avoid

In society, bodybuilding food has a lot of stereotypes, for example, chicken breasts. Most of us know that a handful of staple foods fulfill the strict nutritional needs and provide an anabolic stimulus. But there are a lot of lesser-known foods that are also good for bodybuilding goals.

Add it to your grocery list!

Greek Yogurt

Greek yogurt is made by straining the extra carbohydrates and liquid from regular yogurt, and then yielding a bigger concentration of protein. This straining method used to produce Greek yogurt results in an increased casein concentration ("slow-digesting" protein); thanks to it, the bloodstream is enriched with amino acids.

Depending on how many calories you need, Greek yogurt has two options - full-fat or reduced-fat yogurt. So, you can adapt it to your muscle-building needs. Buy only plain Greek yogurt to avoid added sugar.

Steak

As a bodybuilder, you can get a lot of benefit using saturated fats for your goals. You can find them in steak, eggs, full-fat dairy, and poultry. If you work with weights (especially heavyweights) and follow a high-fat diet, you will get higher test rates than a standard "healthy" lifestyle. You shouldn't increase the level of saturated fats to more than 15 percent of your total calories. Avoid intaking trans fats together with saturated fats so as not to harm your health.

Oatmeal

Fiber retains substantial water and renders food residues "bulk" in the GI tract. Also, fiber causes a "scraping" effect on the gut wall cells. Fiber can dilute or bind harmful chemicals to reduce their activity. It accelerates the speed through the digestive tract of undesired food residues.

Oatmeal is a perfect example of a high fiber food. Only one serving consists of 13 percent of your daily fiber needs. Lack of fiber is a problem for a lot of people and even for professional athletes. It's better not to eat a big amount of fiber before your workouts because of its slow digestion. Eating a high-fiber meal directly after exercise can be harmful because the two hours after exercise are the most critical time to get nutrients readily available to start the process of repair and regeneration. Try to eat high-fiber foods with other dishes during the day. You can get fiber from fruits, whole grains, seeds, vegetables, beans, and nuts.

Beets/Beetroot

The main ability of beets and its juice is increasing the production of nitric oxide in our body, which improves the process of dilating blood vessels that cause better blood flow.

Increased blood flow leads to increased distribution of oxygen and nutrients to the muscles and surrounding tissues. The progress is likely to help improve athletic performance and recovery — which is key to building mass.

Grass-Fed Beef

Beef fed with grass is far superior to standard beef, primarily due to the higher nutrients, for example, CLA. There is one important difference between grass-fed and grain-fed beef. The first one contains 2-5 times more omega-3s than the second one. Grass-fed beef contains a bigger proportion of stearic acid, which doesn't cause blood cholesterol levels to rise.

Bananas

Bananas are a source of the enzyme bromelain, which can boost a man's libido. Bananas enrich our body with riboflavin (B vitamins group). Bromelain was also used to improve indigestion and reduce inflammation in South and Central America for centuries.

Grapes

The skins of red grapes contain polyphenols, as do many fruits and vegetables. These polyphenols help clear our body from free radicals, acting as antioxidants. Free radicals are molecules that can damage our body.

The other feature is resveratrol. It is an aromatase inhibitor. Being an enzyme, aromatase creates estrogen from testosterone and other androgens. This process can be important for people who want to maintain and increase lean mass by reducing estrogen.

Of course, if you want to be a bodybuilder, you need to eat a huge amount of food for gaining muscle. You must understand that not all food will help you. In general, the bodybuilding diet is almost the same as a typical healthy diet, where you intake healthy fats and extra protein for stimulating muscle growth and balancing hormones. You should avoid highly processed food and high-carb foods. Don't trust these foods because of preservatives, sugar and salt, and many others. Be sure they can only slow down your progress.

White Bread

Though white bread has its place in a healthy food pyramid, not all white bread is good for the bodybuilder diet. It not only has a high amount of carbs per serving but also has high fructose corn syrup added to it. It will make you sugar-addicted, which you want to avoid. Fructose has another metabolism process, that is quite different from other sugars, for example, glucose. This could hamper satiation and cause you to eat more carbs than you wanted.

Flavored Oatmeal

As said above, oatmeal is an excellent choice for a bodybuilder breakfast. It is a better source of carbs than any junk food and contains an essential amount of protein, fiber, and unsaturated fat. Today you can see flavored oatmeal in the grocery store. It's not the same thing, and affects the digestion process differently. Flavored varieties contain additives, which are not good in general,. A flavored oatmeal packet includes maltodextrin, sugar, and hydrogenated soybean oil. There is no place for such things in the bodybuilder diet, especially the excess sugar.

Soy Protein

Protein is one of the necessary elements for bodybuilding, and it is important to know which source of protein is reliable and won't damage you. One of these bad protein sources is soy protein. While it contains about 10 g of protein per 126 g serving, it affects negatively on testosterone productive function. Testosterone is one of the most necessary hormones for bodybuilding because it induces muscle growth. You can't count on good results while soy protein affects your body.

Fruit Juice

Refrain from buying concentrated fruit juice. It doesn't have all the nutritional value of the whole fruits. They are highly concentrated sugary drinks without any health benefits such as fiber or other nutrients. It's better to avoid the intake such juices if you are following a bodybuilder diet and instead make your own juices or smoothies from fresh whole fruits at home. Just buy yourself a blender or juicer and prepare some bags with fruit mix. It will be a much better alternative for your health and body.

We suggest you try this meal prep plan to help with muscle building. The meal plan is calculated for people who are underweight and want to gain weight. It is based on simple foods that you can easily find in a local grocery store. It's perfect for people who need nutrition for bodybuilding workouts.

Week 1

Days 1-5 provide about 3000 calories. You can expect to gain 1-2lbs of weight per week. Of course, we can't guarantee it, because all depends on individual features (body size, activity level, gender).

Days 6 and 7 provide 4000 calories. You should follow these days only if you're training regularly and want to increase your muscle mass. Don't follow it if you don't want to gain muscle weight because the result won't be good.

CONSULT A PERSONAL TRAINER OR NUTRITIONIST BEFORE STARTING ANY MEAL PLAN AND WORKOUTS!

Breakfast

Berry Parfait (p. 40)
1 glass Orange juice

Calories - 554	Carbohydrates – 78 g
	Fat – 43 g
	Protein – 27 g

Snack 1

1 Banana

Calories - 105	Carbohydrates – 3 g
	Fat – 14 g
	Protein – 4 g

Lunch

Pork Green Chili (p. 63)

Calories - 676	Carbohydrates – 79 g
	Fat – 42 g
	Protein – 28 g

Snack 2

Unsalted Nuts (25 g)

Calories - 160	Carbohydrates – 3 g
	Fat – 14 g
	Protein – 4 g

Dinner

Cashew Chicken (p. 52)
3 slices Wheat toast with Peanut Butter

Calories - 1114	Carbohydrates – 68 g
	Fat – 11 g
	Protein – 36 g

Dessert

Chocolate Peanut Butter Chia Pudding (p. 101)

Calories - 301	Carbohydrates – 18 g
	Fat – 20 g
	Protein – 11 g

Day 2

Breakfast

Overnights Oats (p. 39)
2 Bananas
1 glass Orange juice

Calories - 755	Carbohydrates – 124 g
	Fat – 17 g
	Protein – 24 g

Snack 1

1 Apple + 1 tbsp Peanut Butter

Calories - 222	Carbohydrates – 29 g
	Fat – 8 g
	Protein – 5 g

Lunch

Pork Green Chili (p. 63)
Garlic Sweet Potatoes (p. 74)

Calories - 897	Carbohydrates – 113 g
	Fat – 49 g
	Protein – 31 g

Snack 2

1 Avocado + 4-5 Crackers

Calories - 445	Carbohydrates – 35 g
	Fat – 31 g
	Protein – 7 g

Dinner

BBQ Chicken and Rice (p. 55)

Calories - 511	Carbohydrates – 57 g
	Fat – 6 g
	Protein – 41 g

Day 3

Breakfast

Berry Parfait (p. 40)
Orange juice 1 glass

Calories - 554	Carbohydrates – 101 g
	Fat – 33 g
	Protein – 24 g

Snack 1

Granola Bar

Calories - 119	Carbohydrates – 15 g
	Fat – 6 g
	Protein – 2 g

Lunch

Kale White Bean Chicken Soup (p. 47)
1 glass Orange juice

Calories - 939	Carbohydrates – 76 g
	Fat – 36 g
	Protein – 75 g

Snack 2

1 Banana
1 Wheat toast

Calories - 193	Carbohydrates – 42 g
	Fat – 1 g
	Protein – 5 g

Dinner

Mango Cod (p. 76)

Calories - 400	Carbohydrates – 60 g
	Fat – 5 g
	Protein – 28 g

Dessert

Chocolate Peanut Butter Chia Pudding (p. 101)

Calories - 301	Carbohydrates – 18 g
	Fat – 20 g
	Protein – 11 g

Breakfast

Berry Parfait (p. 40)
Orange juice 1 glass

Calories - 554	Carbohydrates – 101 g Fat – 33 g Protein – 24 g

Snack 1

1 Banana

Calories - 105	Carbohydrates – 3 g Fat – 14 g Protein – 4 g

Lunch

Pork Green Chili (p. 58)

Calories - 676	Carbohydrates – 79 g Fat – 42 g Protein – 28 g

Snack 2

Unsalted Nuts (25 g)

Calories - 160	Carbohydrates – 3 g Fat – 14 g Protein – 4 g

Dinner

Cashew Chicken (p. 52)
3 slices Wheat toast with Peanut Butter

Calories - 715	Carbohydrates – 40 g Fat – 40 g Protein – 82 g

Breakfast

Turkey Bacon Breakfast (p. 44)
Breakfast Sandwich (p. 38)
1 glass Orange juice

Calories - 743	Carbohydrates – 101 g
	Fat – 33 g
	Protein – 24 g

Snack 1

1 Apple + 1 tbsp Peanut Butter

Calories - 222	Carbohydrates – 29 g
	Fat – 8 g
	Protein – 5 g

Lunch

Kale White Bean Chicken Soup (p. 47)
1 glass Orange juice

Calories - 939	Carbohydrates – 76 g
	Fat – 36 g
	Protein – 75 g

Snack 2

1 Avocado + 4-5 Crackers

Calories – 445	Carbohydrates – 35 g
	Fat – 31 g
	Protein – 7 g

Dinner

Mango Cod (p. 76)

Calories - 400	Carbohydrates – 60 g
	Fat – 5 g
	Protein – 28 g

Dessert

Chocolate Peanut Butter Chia Pudding (p. 101)

Calories - 301	Carbohydrates – 18 g
	Fat – 20 g
	Protein – 11 g

Day 6

Breakfast

Turkey Bacon Breakfast (p. 44)
Breakfast Sandwich (p. 38)
1 glass Orange juice

Calories - 743	Carbohydrates – 101 g
	Fat – 33 g
	Protein – 24 g

Snack 1

1 Banana
1 Whole-Wheat bread slice + 1 tbsp peanut butter

Calories - 305	Carbohydrates – 42 g
	Fat – 9 g
	Protein – 9 g

Lunch

Buffalo Chicken (p. 58)
Vegetarian Veggie Bowls (p. 98)

Calories - 883	Carbohydrates – 62 g
	Fat – 39 g
	Protein – 68 g

Snack 2

Unsalted Nuts (25 g)
9 Apricots (dried)

Calories - 380	Carbohydrates – 46 g
	Fat – 18g
	Protein – 8 g

Dinner

Full Harvest Quinoa Salad (p. 88)
Peanut Butter Chicken (p. 54)

Calories – 1196	Carbohydrates – 118 g
	Fat – 48 g
	Protein – 64 g

Day 7

Breakfast

Banana Egg Pancakes (p. 45) + Toppings
Orange juice 1

Calories – 1052	Carbohydrates – 141 g
	Fat – 38 g
	Protein – 38 g

Snack 1

Cheese (30 g) + 4-5 Crackers

Calories – 203	Carbohydrates – 12 g
	Fat – 11 g
	Protein – 9 g

Lunch

Full Harvest Quinoa Salad (p. 88)
Peanut Butter Chicken (p. 54)

Calories – 1196	Carbohydrates – 118 g
	Fat – 48 g
	Protein – 64 g

Snack 2

Granola (50 g)
Whole Milk (150 g)

Calories – 315	Carbohydrates – 38 g
	Fat – 9 g
	Protein – 13 g

Dinner

Buffalo Chicken (p. 58)
Vegetarian Veggie Bowls (p. 98)

Calories – 883	Carbohydrates – 62 g
	Fat – 39 g
	Protein – 68 g

Dessert

Chocolate Peanut Butter Chia Pudding (p. 101)

Calories – 301	Carbohydrates – 18 g
	Fat – 20 g
	Protein – 11 g

Week 2

Day 1

Breakfast

Sweet Potato Hash (p. 46)	
Asian Chicken Mason Jar (p. 87)	
Calories – 876	*Carbohydrates – 55 g* *Fat – 49 g* *Protein – 56 g*

Snack 1

Cheese (30 g) + 4-5 Crackers	
Calories - 203	*Carbohydrates – 12 g* *Fat – 11 g* *Protein – 9 g*

Lunch

Buffalo Chicken (p. 58)	
Power Up Bowl (p. 99)	
Calories - 822	*Carbohydrates – 57 g* *Fat – 43 g* *Protein – 59 g*

Snack 2

Hummus and Veggie Snack Box (p. 92)	
Calories - 198	Carbohydrates – 7 g Fat – 6 g Protein – 27 g

Dinner

Tuna and Sweet Potatoes (p. 69)	
Vegetarian Veggie Bowls (p. 98)	
Calories - 764	*Carbohydrates – 40 g* *Fat – 14 g* *Protein – 65 g*

Snack 3

1 Banana	
Calories - 105	*Carbohydrates – 27 g* *Fat – 0 g* *Protein – 1 g*

Breakfast

Turkey Bacon Breakfast (p. 44)
2 sliced Buttered Toast
Orange juice 1 glass

Calories - 671	Carbohydrates – 67 g
	Fat – 24 g
	Protein – 27 g

Snack 1

1 Pear
Pumpkin Seeds (28 g)

Calories - 226	Carbohydrates – 26 g
	Fat – 11 g
	Protein – 10 g

Lunch

Baked Lemon Cod (p. 74)
Quinoa Burrito Bowls (p. 94)

Calories - 745	Carbohydrates – 63 g
	Fat – 33 g
	Protein – 55 g

Snack 2

Hummus and Veggie Snack Box (p. 92)

Calories - 198	Carbohydrates – 7 g
	Fat – 6 g
	Protein – 27 g

Dinner

Shrimp Green Goddess Grain Bowl (p. 73)
Peanut Butter Chicken (p. 54)

Calories – 912	Carbohydrates – 95 g
	Fat – 34 g
	Protein – 68 g

Day 3

Breakfast

Sweet Potato Hash (p. 46)
Asian Chicken Mason Jar (p. 87)

Calories – 876	*Carbohydrates – 55 g*
	Fat – 49 g
	Protein – 56 g

Snack 1

Granola (50 g)
Whole Milk (150 g)

Calories – 315	*Carbohydrates – 38 g*
	Fat – 9 g
	Protein – 13 g

Lunch

Buffalo Chicken (p. 58)
Power Up Bowl (p. 99)

Calories - 822	*Carbohydrates – 57 g*
	Fat – 43 g
	Protein – 59 g

Snack 2

Unsalted Nuts (25 g)

Calories – 160	*Carbohydrates – 15 g*
	Fat – 9 g
	Protein – 8 g

Dinner

Shrimp Green Goddess Grain Bowl (p. 73)
Peanut Butter Chicken (p. 54)

Calories – 912	*Carbohydrates – 95 g*
	Fat – 34 g
	Protein – 68 g

Snack 3

Hummus and Veggie Snack Box (p. 92)

Calories - 198	*Carbohydrates – 7 g*
	Fat – 6 g
	Protein – 27 g

Day 4

Breakfast

Middle-Eastern Box (p. 41)
Orange juice 1 glass

Calories - 615	Carbohydrates – 51g
	Fat – 30 g
	Protein – 31 g

Snack 1

1 Banana
1 Whole-Wheat bread slice + 1 tbsp peanut butter

Calories - 305	Carbohydrates – 42 g
	Fat – 9 g
	Protein – 9 g

Lunch

Baked Lemon Cod (p. 74)
Quinoa Burrito Bowls (p. 94)

Calories – 745	Carbohydrates – 63 g
	Fat – 33 g
	Protein – 55 g

Snack 1

1 Pear
Pumpkin Seeds (28 g)

Calories – 226	Carbohydrates – 26 g
	Fat – 11 g
	Protein – 10 g

Dinner

Shrimp Green Goddess Grain Bowl (p. 73)
Peanut Butter Chicken (p. 54)

Calories – 912	Carbohydrates – 95 g
	Fat – 34 g
	Protein – 68 g

Day 5

Breakfast

Turkey Bacon Breakfast (p. 44)
Breakfast Sandwich (p. 38)
Orange juice 1 glass

Calories – 743	Carbohydrates – 101 g
	Fat – 33 g
	Protein – 24 g

Snack 1

Granola (50 g)
Whole Milk (150 g)

Calories – 315	Carbohydrates – 38 g
	Fat – 9 g
	Protein – 13 g

Lunch

Italian Couscous Salad (p. 86)

Calories – 547	Carbohydrates – 51 g
	Fat – 30 g
	Protein – 20 g

Snack 2

Unsalted Nuts (25 g) + 1 Banana

Calories – 265	Carbohydrates – 18 g
	Fat – 23 g
	Protein – 12 g

Dinner

Full Harvest Quinoa Salad (p.88)
Peanut Butter Chicken (p. 54)

Calories – 1196	Carbohydrates – 118 g
	Fat – 48 g
	Protein – 64 g

Snack 3

Hummus and Veggie Snack Box (p. 92)

Calories - 198	Carbohydrates – 7 g
	Fat – 6 g
	Protein – 27 g

Day 6

Breakfast

Banana Egg Pancakes (p. 45) + Toppings
Orange juice 1 glass

Calories – 1052	Carbohydrates – 141 g
	Fat – 38 g
	Protein – 38 g

Snack 1

Unsalted Nuts (50 g)

Calories - 320	Carbohydrates – 5 g
	Fat – 28 g
	Protein – 8 g

Lunch

Full Harvest Quinoa Salad (p. 88)
Peanut Butter Chicken (p. 54)

Calories – 1196	Carbohydrates – 118 g
	Fat – 48 g
	Protein – 64 g

Snack 2

Granola (50 g)
Whole Milk (150 g)

Calories – 315	Carbohydrates – 38 g
	Fat – 9 g
	Protein – 13 g

Dinner

Asian Chicken Mason Jar (p. 87)
Skirt Steak (p. 68)

Calories – 1259	Carbohydrates – 91 g
	Fat – 69 g
	Protein – 81 g

Day 7

Breakfast

Banana Egg Pancakes (p. 45) + Toppings
Orange juice 1 glass

Calories – 1052	Carbohydrates – 141 g
	Fat – 38 g
	Protein – 38 g

Snack 1

Unsalted Nuts (50 g) + Berries Detox Smoothie

Calories - 542	Carbohydrates – 52 g
	Fat – 31 g
	Protein – 31 g

Lunch

Full Harvest Quinoa Salad (p. 88)
Peanut Butter Chicken (p. 54)

Calories – 1196	Carbohydrates – 118 g
	Fat – 48 g
	Protein – 64 g

Snack 2

2 Bananas

Calories – 210	Carbohydrates – 6 g
	Fat – 28 g
	Protein – 8 g

Dinner

Asian Chicken Mason Jar (p. 87)
Skirt Steak (p. 68)

Calories – 1259	Carbohydrates – 91 g
	Fat – 69 g
	Protein – 81 g

Snack 3

Hummus and Veggie Snack Box (p. 92)

Calories - 198	Carbohydrates – 7 g
	Fat – 6 g
	Protein – 27 g

CHAPTER 3. Recipes
BREAKFAST
Breakfast Sandwich

Prep time: 15 minutes

Cooking time: 15 minutes

Servings: 10-12

NUTRIENTS PER SERVING:

Carbohydrates – 27 g

Fat – 11 g

Protein – 13 g

Calories – 267 g

INGREDIENTS:

- 12 eggs
- ¼ cup whole milk
- 1½ tsp salt
- 6 slices bacon, cut
- A few handfuls of spinach
- 12 English muffins
- Cheese (optional)
- Butter (optional)

INSTRUCTIONS:

1. Preheat the oven to 300°F.
2. Grease a rimmed sheet pan with oil.
3. Mix the eggs, milk and salt in a bowl.
4. Add bacon and fry until crispy.
5. Add spinach and stir well.
6. Allow the fat drip off the bacon and spinach. Add to the eggs.
7. Pour the egg mixture into the pan.
8. Bake for 15 minutes.
9. Take out and let it cool. Cut into rounds.
10. Spread the muffins with butter.
11. Put an egg on each muffin.
12. Add the cheese and wrap in foil.
13. Store in the fridge for 4-5 days.
14. Enjoy!

Overnight Oats

Prep time: 5 minutes

Cooking time: 5 minutes + overnight

Servings: 1

NUTRIENTS PER SERVING:

Carbohydrates – 45 g

Fat – 17 g

Protein – 10 g

Calories – 372

INGREDIENTS:

- 75 g dairy-free yogurt
- 1 tbsp All-Natural Almond Butter
- 50 g 100% Instant Oats
- 125 ml almond milk
- 1 pinch almonds, crushed
- 1 tsp cinnamon
- 1 pinch salt

INSTRUCTIONS:

1. Add all the ingredients to the jar or bowl.
2. Mix well to combine all of the ingredients.
3. Cover and put it the fridge overnight.
4. Enjoy!

Berry Parfait

Prep time: 10 minutes

Cooking time: 10 minutes

Servings: 2

NUTRIENTS PER SERVING:

Carbohydrates – 61 g

Fat – 13 g

Protein – 25 g

Calories – 438

INGREDIENTS:

- 12 oz. 2% plain Greek yogurt
- 2 tsp maple syrup
- ⅔ cup granola
- ⅓ cup blueberries
- ⅓ cup raspberries

INSTRUCTIONS:

1. Combine the greek yogurt and maple syrup in a bowl and mix well.
2. Layer the ingredients in the jar starting with the yogurt.
3. Then add the berries. Repeat.
4. Top with granola and cover.
5. Store in the fridge and eat within 1-2 days.
6. Enjoy!

Middle-Eastern Box

Prep time: 15 minutes

Cooking time: 15 minutes

Servings: 4

NUTRIENTS PER SERVING:

Carbohydrates – 36 g

Fat – 30 g

Protein – 28 g

Calories – 490

INGREDIENTS:

- 1 cup cucumber, sliced
- 2 whole-wheat pita, cut in quarters
- 1 cup cherry tomatoes, cut in half
- 1 cup onion, cut
- 2 tbsp feta cheese
- ½ cup olives
- 4-8 falafel
- 1 15-oz can garbanzo beans, drained, + 2 tbsp liquid reserved
- 2 tbsp tahini sauce
- 1 tbsp lemon juice
- 1 tbsp olive oil
- 1 clove garlic crushed
- ½ tsp ground cumin

INSTRUCTIONS:

1. Add the garbanzo beans, tahini sauce, lemon juice, oil, garlic, cumin and salt to a food processor to make the hummus.
2. Put little portions (¼ cup) of hummus into each box or into the small sauce boxes.
3. Prepare the vegetables and cheese. Mix or keep them separate.
4. Put the veggies into each container.
5. Add the 2 pita slices and 1-2 falafel to each container. Cover.
6. Put in the fridge and refrigerate for up to 4 days.
7. Enjoy!

Protein Waffles

Prep time: 5 minutes

Cooking time: 12 minutes

Servings: 4

NUTRIENTS PER SERVING:

Carbohydrates – 27 g

Fat – 21 g

Protein – 11 g

Calories – 331

INGREDIENTS:

- 1 cup old fashioned oats
- 1 tsp honey
- 3 eggs
- 1 cup cottage cheese
- 1 tsp vanilla extra
- ½ tsp baking powder
- For meal prepping:
- 1 cup berries
- ½ cup preferred topping

INSTRUCTIONS:

1. Turn on and preheat the waffle iron.
2. Use a cooking spray to cover it.
3. Add the oats, cottage cheese, eggs, honey, vanilla and baking powder to a blender to make a smooth mixture.

4. Pour enough mixture to make 1 waffle in your waffle iron. Cook until it turns off.
5. Repeat for the rest of the batter.
6. Divide the waffles and put them into 4 containers.
7. Add ¼ cup of berries and a few spoons of your chosen topping to waffles.
8. Keep in the fridge for 3-4 days.
9. Enjoy!

Fruits and Yogurt Box

Prep time: 15 minutes

Cooking time: 15 minutes

Servings: 4

NUTRIENTS PER SERVING:

Carbohydrates – 14 g

Fat – 1 g

Protein – 3 g

Calories – 129

INGREDIENTS:

- 1¾ cup vanilla or plain greek yogurt
- 5 cup mixed fruits (strawberry, grapes, blackberries), divided into 4 portions

INSTRUCTIONS:

1. Divide the yogurt evenly and add to each container.
2. Add 1 ¼ cup berries to each container.
3. Cover with lid.
4. Store in the fridge for 3-4 days.
5. Enjoy!

Turkey Bacon Breakfast

Prep time: 1 minute

Cooking time: 30

Servings: 2

NUTRIENTS PER SERVING:

Carbohydrates – 17 g

Fat – 24 g

Protein – 22 g

Calories – 360

INGREDIENTS:

- 4 eggs
- 2 large sweet potatoes, diced
- 2 tsp heavy cream
- 1 tbsp olive oil
- 1 cup broccoli florets, cooked
- 2 garlic cloves, minced
- ¼ tsp thyme
- ¼ tsp salt
- ¼ tsp black pepper
- 4 slices turkey bacon

INSTRUCTIONS:

1. Mix the eggs, cream, salt and pepper in a bowl.
2. Preheat the oven to 400°F.
3. Coat the baking sheet with nonstick spray.
4. Arrange potatoes in one layer on the baking sheet.

5. Add the oil, garlic, thyme, salt and pepper to taste. Toss well to coat the potatoes.
6. Bake for 25-30 minutes. Set aside.
7. Heat a skillet over a medium-low heat.
8. Pour the egg mixture into the pan.
9. Cook with a spatula until it's done. Set aside.
10. Clean the skillet and heat it again.
11. Cook the bacon slices how you like them.
12. Allow all of the ingredients to cool.
13. Divide evenly between 2 containers.
14. Store in the fridge for 3-4 days. Enjoy!

Banana Egg Pancakes

Prep time: 5 minutes

Cooking time: 20 minutes

Servings: 16-20 pancakes

NUTRIENTS PER SERVING:

Carbohydrates – 40 g

Fat – 13 g

Protein – 18 g

Calories – 342

INGREDIENTS:

- 8 eggs
- 4 bananas
- Preferred fruit
- Maple syrup for serving

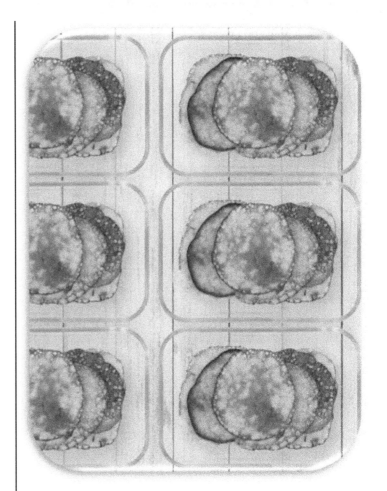

INSTRUCTIONS:

1. Mash bananas in a bowl.
2. Add the eggs and whisk.
3. Heat the butter over a medium heat in a pan.
4. Add the batter to the pan to make pancakes.
5. Cook for 3-4 minutes on each side.
6. Divide between the meal prep containers with your chosen fruits.
7. Store in the fridge for 5 days.
8. Enjoy!

Sweet Potato Hash

Prep time: 20 minutes

Cooking time: 20 minutes

Servings: 4

NUTRIENTS PER SERVING:

Carbohydrates –26 g

Fat – 16 g

Protein – 27 g

Calories – 352

INGREDIENTS:

- 1 tbsp olive oil
- 2 medium-sized sweet potatoes, diced
- 1 each red, green and yellow pepper, diced
- 1 medium-sized red onion, diced
- 1 cup kale, chopped
- 1 tbsp chili powder
- ½ tsp each salt and pepper
- 1 lb. ground turkey

Spices for the meat:

- 2 cloves garlic, minced
- 2 tsp dijon mustard
- 2 tsp fennel seeds
- 2 tsp smoked paprika
- 2 tsp onion powder
- ½ tsp each salt and pepper

INSTRUCTIONS:

1. Preheat the oil over a medium-high heat.

2. Add the potatoes, ½ chili powder and salt.
3. Cook for 15-20 minutes, stirring.
4. Season the turkey with the spices for the meat and add to the potatoes. Cook for 5-7 minutes.
5. Add the bell peppers, onions, chili powder, salt and pepper. Cook for 5 minutes.
6. Add the kale. Remove from heat.
7. Allow to cool.
8. Divide between 4 glass containers.
9. Store in the fridge for 4-5 days.
10. Serve with fried eggs.
11. Enjoy!

SOUPS

Kale White Beans Chicken Soup

Prep time: 10 minutes
Cooking time: 20 minutes
Servings: 8

NUTRIENTS PER SERVING:

Carbohydrates – 51 g
Fat – 36 g
Protein – 75 g
Calories – 823

INGREDIENTS:

- 3 tbsp olive oil
- 2 cups yellow onion, peeled and diced small
- 1 cup celery, sliced thin
- 2 cup green cabbage, sliced into thin ribbons
- 4 garlic cloves, peeled and minced
- 8 cup low-sodium chicken broth
- 3-4 cups shredded cooked chicken
- 2 15-oz cans cannellini beans, drained and rinsed
- 1 tbsp dried parsley
- 1 tsp dried oregano
- 1 tsp salt
- 1 tsp black pepper
- 4 stalks kale leaves, torn into bite-sized pieces
- 1 cup zucchini, diced

INSTRUCTIONS:

1. Add the oil, onion and celery to the preheated stockpot.

2. Cook over a medium-high heat for 7 minutes, stirring.
3. Add the cabbage. Cook for 3 minutes.
4. Add the garlic. Cook for 1-2 minutes.
5. Add the broth, shredded chicken, cannellini beans, parsley, oregano, salt and pepper.
6. Let it boil for 5 minutes.
7. Add the kale and zucchini. Boil for 1-2 minutes.
8. Taste the soup and adjust spices to taste.
9. Allow the soup to cool.
10. Divide soup evenly into glass jars and cover tightly.
11. Store in the fridge for 1 week.
12. Enjoy!

Tomato Soup

Prep time: 10 minutes

Cooking time: 20 minutes

Servings: 6

NUTRIENTS PER SERVING:

Carbohydrates – 15 g

Fat – 2 g

Protein – 2 g

Calories – 90

INGREDIENTS:

- 1 small yellow onion, chopped
- 1 tbsp extra-virgin olive oil
- 2 garlic cloves, minced
- ½ tsp crushed red pepper flakes
- 2 tbsp tomato paste
- 1 tsp thyme leaves
- 2 cans whole peeled tomatoes
- Kosher salt to taste
- Black pepper to taste
- 2 cups water

INSTRUCTIONS:

1. Preheat the oil in a pot over a medium heat.
2. Add the onion. Cook for 6 minutes.
3. Add the garlic, red pepper flakes and tomato paste. Cook for 2-3 minutes.
4. Add the thyme, 2 cans tomatoes + juice.
5. Add the water and let it simmer. Cook for 10 minutes.
6. Blend the soup until smooth.
7. Let the soup cool down.
8. Divide the soup evenly into glass jars and cover tightly.
9. Store in the fridge for 1 week. Enjoy!

Detox Soup

Prep time: 15 minutes

Cooking time: 15 minutes

Servings: 4

NUTRIENTS PER SERVING:

Carbohydrates – 27 g

Fat – 1 g

Protein – 3 g

Calories – 114

INGREDIENTS:

- 6 cups vegetable broth
- ¼ cup water (additional)
- ½ red onion, diced
- 2 cloves garlic, minced
- 3 celery stalks, diced
- 3 carrots, cut into circles
- 1 small head of broccoli, florets
- 1 cup tomatoes, cut in half
- 1 cup spinach
- 1 tbsp fresh ginger, minced
- 1 tsp turmeric powder
- ¼ tsp cinnamon
- ⅛ tsp cayenne pepper
- Sea salt and black pepper, to taste
- 2 cups kale, de-stemmed and torn in pieces
- 1 cup purple cabbage, chopped
- ½ lemon juice

INSTRUCTIONS:

1. Add and heat a little of the water in a large pot over a medium-high heat.
2. Add the onion and garlic. Cook for 2 minutes, stirring.
3. Add the celery, broccoli, tomatoes, ginger, and carrots. Cook for 3 minutes. Add extra water if needed.
4. Add the turmeric, cinnamon, cayenne pepper, salt and pepper. Mix well
5. Pour in the broth and let it boil.
6. Reduce the heat. Simmer for 15 minutes.
7. Add in the kale, cabbage and lemon juice. Simmer for 2-3 minutes.
8. Divide the soup evenly into glass jars and cover tightly.
9. Store in the fridge for 1 week. Enjoy!

Spring Pea and Mint Soup

Prep time: 10 minutes

Cooking time: 15 minutes

Servings: 3

NUTRIENTS PER SERVING:

Carbohydrates – 23 g

Fat – 5 g

Protein – 8 g

Calories – 164

INGREDIENTS:

- 1 tbsp extra virgin olive oil
- 1 stalk celery, chopped
- 1 medium onion, chopped
- ½ clove garlic, chopped
- 1 cube vegetable stock
- 3 ¼ cup water
- 14 ounces fresh or frozen peas
- 1 small bunch of fresh mint
- Salt to taste
- Freshly ground black pepper

INSTRUCTIONS:

1. Preheat the oil in a pan over a high heat.
2. Add the celery, onion, and garlic. Cook for 5 minutes, stirring.
3. Dissolve the stock with the hot water into a jug.
4. Add the stock and peas to the vegetables.
5. Stir and bring to the boil. Reduce the heat.
6. Cover with lid and let it simmer for 10 minutes. Let the peas soften.
7. Turn off the heat.
8. Add the salt and pepper. Add the mint leaves.
9. Make into a smooth soup using a blender.
10. Divide the soup evenly into glass jars and cover tightly.
11. Store in the fridge for 1 week.
12. Enjoy!

Zoodle Ramen

Prep time: 15 minutes

Cooking time: 315 minutes

Servings: 4

NUTRIENTS PER SERVING:

Carbohydrates – 41 g

Fat – 14 g

Protein – 11 g

Calories – 415

INGREDIENTS:

- 4 eggs, boiled
- 1 tbsp extra-virgin olive oil
- 8 oz cremini mushrooms, sliced
- 1 tsp fresh ginger, minced
- 4 cloves garlic, minced
- 4 zucchinis, cut into noodles
- 8 cups bone broth
- 1 tbsp low-sodium soy sauce
- 1 tbsp sesame oil
- 2 green onions, sliced
- ½ cup red cabbage, chopped
- 1 cup carrots, shredded
- 2 tbsp sesame seeds, toasted
- 1 pinch crushed red pepper flakes

INSTRUCTIONS:

1. Heat the oil in a skillet over a medium heat.
2. Add the mushrooms. Cook for 5 minutes.
3. Add the garlic and ginger. Cook for 1 minute.
4. Add the bone broth, soy sauce, and bring to a boil. Reduce the heat and simmer for 5 minutes.
5. Add the zucchini noodles. Cook for 2 minutes. Add the sesame oil and mix well.
6. Divide the carrots, cabbage, and hardboiled eggs among each jar.
7. Divide the soup evenly into the glass jars and cover tightly.
8. Store in the fridge for 1 week.
9. Enjoy!

POULTRY

Cashew Chicken

Prep time: 10 minutes

Cooking time: 30 minutes

Servings: 4

NUTRIENTS PER SERVING:

Carbohydrates – 68 g

Fat – 11 g

Protein – 36 g

Calories – 527

INGREDIENTS:

- 3 tbsp cashew butter
- 2 tbsp soy sauce
- 2 tbsp maple syrup
- 2 cloves garlic
- 1 tsp Chinese five-spice
- 4 chicken breasts, diced
- 1 cup broccoli florets
- 40 g cashew nuts, toasted
- 2 red chilies, diced
- Handful fresh coriander
- 300g basmati rice, cooked

INSTRUCTIONS:

1. Preheat the oven to 375°F.
2. Mix the cashew butter, soy sauce, maple syrup, garlic, and five-spice in a large bowl.

3. Add the chicken and broccoli florets to the bowl and toss well to coat them.
4. Put the ingredients into a deep baking tray. Cook for 20 minutes.
5. Add the toasted cashews and chilies to the chicken.
6. Put the basmati rice and chicken along with the vegetables into the containers.
7. Cover and put it to the fridge.
8. Enjoy!

prep   easy

taste   8/10

Chicken with Sweet Potato and Green Beans

Prep time: 10 minutes

Cooking time: 20 minutes

Servings: 4

NUTRIENTS PER SERVING:

Carbohydrates – 37 g

Fat – 8 g

Protein – 47 g

Calories – 400

INGREDIENTS:

- 2 tbsp coconut oil
- 4 chicken breasts, sliced
- 350g sweet potato, cut into wedges
- ½ tsp sea salt
- ½ tsp black pepper
- ½ tsp paprika
- 350g green beans, trimmed
- 1 pinch of preferred spices

INSTRUCTIONS:

1. Preheat the oven to 375°F.
2. Put the potatoes onto a baking tray. Season with spices and bake for 25 minutes.
3. Blanch the green beans with a pinch of salt for 1-2 minutes.
4. Put the chicken in a frying pan over a medium heat.
5. Brown on all sides and season with spices. Set aside.
6. Drain the green beans. Allow all the ingredients to cool.
7. Add a scoop of wedges, green beans, chicken to each container.
8. Cover and store in the fridge. Enjoy!

Peanut Butter Chicken

Prep time: 5 minutes

Cooking time: 15 minutes

Servings: 4

NUTRIENTS PER SERVING:

Carbohydrates – 39 g

Fat – 20 g

Protein – 40 g

Calories – 489

INGREDIENTS:

- 5 tbsp peanut butter
- 50 ml orange juice
- 100 ml hot water
- 3 tbsp sugar-free syrup
- 3 tbsp soy sauce
- 1 thumb ginger, grated
- Salt to taste
- 3 chicken breasts
- 1 cup broccoli florets, cooked
- 2 carrots, thinly sliced
- 300 g rice, cooked (optional)

INSTRUCTIONS:

1. Preheat the oven to 375°F.
2. Mix the peanut butter, water, and orange juice until smooth. Add in the syrup, soy sauce, and ginger. Stir well and set aside.

3. In a non-stick pan sear the chicken over a high heat for 3 minutes each side.
4. Transfer the meat to a casserole dish and coat with the peanut butter sauce.
5. Bake for 20 minutes.
6. Mix the syrup, soy, sesame oil and seeds to make the salad dressing.
7. Combine the carrots and broccoli with dressing.
8. Make 4 portions and put into airtight containers.
9. Cover and store in the fridge.
10. Enjoy!

BBQ Chicken and Rice

Prep time: 10 minutes

Cooking time: 20 minutes

Servings: 4

NUTRIENTS PER SERVING:

Carbohydrates – 57 g

Fat – 6 g

Protein – 41 g

Calories – 511

INGREDIENTS:

- 1 tbsp coconut oil
- 450 g white rice, cooked
- 600 g chicken breast, sliced
- 1 cup broccoli florets, boiled
- 3 tbsp barbecue sauce
- 1 tsp sweet paprika

5/1/22

TASTE - 7.5/10
PREP - quick + easy

INSTRUCTIONS:

1. Toss the chicken with the barbecue sauce, paprika, salt, and pepper.
2. Heat the coconut oil in a hot frying pan.
3. Add the chicken. Cook each side for 4 minutes over a medium heat.
4. Transfer the cooked chicken to a plate to cool the meat down.
5. Add ¼ cup broccoli and a portion of rice to each container.
6. Add the chicken and put the containers in the fridge. Store for 3 days.
7. Enjoy!

Cilantro Lime Chicken with Rice

Prep time: 20 minutes

Cooking time: 30 minutes

Servings: 4

NUTRIENTS PER SERVING:

Carbohydrates – 16 g

Fat – 21 g

Protein – 32 g

Calories – 378

INGREDIENTS:

- 1 lb. boneless, skinless chicken breast
- 2 tbsp olive oil
- Salt and pepper, to taste
- ¼ cup lime juice
- ⅓ cup fresh cilantro, chopped
- 2 tsp garlic, minced
- ⅛ tsp sea salt
- ½ tsp honey

For the cauliflower rice:

- 2 tbsp olive oil
- 3 cups cauliflower rice
- 2 tsp garlic powder
- 1 tsp ground cumin
- ⅛ tsp sea salt

INSTRUCTIONS:

1. Preheat the oil in a skillet over a medium heat.

2. Add the chicken. Cook for 8 minutes each side. Let the meat cool when it's done.
3. Dice the chicken and set aside.
4. Mix the chicken, spices, garlic, and honey in a bowl. Stir well to coat the meat.
5. Preheat the oil in a skillet over a medium heat.
6. Add the rice and spices. Cook for 7 minutes.
7. Allow the rice to cool.
8. Divide all of the ingredients into 4 air-tight containers.
9. Cover and store in the fridge for 4-5 days. Enjoy!

Greek Chicken and Rice

Prep time: 30 minutes

Cooking time: 30 minutes

Servings: 4

NUTRIENTS PER SERVING:

Carbohydrates – 23 g

Fat – 17 g

Protein – 44 g

Calories – 418

INGREDIENTS:

- ½ lbs. boneless, skinless chicken breasts
- 2 tbsp red wine vinegar
- 2 tbsp fresh lemon juice
- 1 tbsp extra virgin olive oil
- 3 cloves garlic, minced
- 2 tsp dried oregano
- 1¼ cups brown rice, cooked
- 2 cups chicken broth
- 1 dry pint grape tomatoes
- 1 cucumber, peeled, seeded and cut into bite-sized pieces
- 1 orange bell pepper, cut into 1-inch pieces
- 20 pitted Kalamata olives, sliced
- 4 tsp extra virgin olive oil
- 1 medium lemon, quartered
- ¼ cup crumbled feta cheese

INSTRUCTIONS:

1. Combine the lemon juice, vinegar, olive oil, garlic, and oregano in a bowl.

2. Put 1 breast in a Ziploc bag and pound it using a mallet. Repeat for the rest of the meat.
3. Pour the marinade into the bag.
4. Marinate for 30 minutes.
5. Preheat the oil a skillet over a medium heat. Add chicken.
6. Cook until it's done (5-6 minutes for each side). Let the meat rest.
7. Divide all of the ingredients into 4 air-tight containers.
8. Cover and store in the fridge for 4-5 days. Enjoy!

Buffalo Chicken

Prep time: 10 minutes

Cooking time: 5 minutes

Servings: 6

NUTRIENTS PER SERVING:

Carbohydrates – 22 g

Fat – 24 g

Protein – 43 g

Calories – 461

INGREDIENTS:

- 1 lb. skinless, boneless chicken breasts
- 1 red pepper, diced

For the sauce:

- ¼ cup Franks buffalo sauce
- 1 tbsp lime juice
- 2 tbsp honey
- 2 tbsp chicken broth
- 1 tsp garlic powder
- 1 tsp chili powder
- ½ tsp onion powder
- ½ tsp cumin
- ½ tsp paprika
- ½ tsp salt
- ¼ tsp pepper

For the salad:

- 2 avocados, diced
- 1 cup grape tomatoes, halved
- 1 handful bof green onion, chopped

INSTRUCTIONS:

1. Put the chicken and red pepper into the slow cooker.
2. Mix all of the ingredients for the buffalo sauce in a bowl. Set aside a quarter of the sauce.
3. Pour the rest of the sauce over the chicken and toss to coat the meat.
4. Set to 3 hours of high pressure.
5. When it's done, shred the meat with forks.
6. Divide all of the ingredients into 4 airtight containers.
7. Cover and store in the fridge for 4-5 days. Enjoy!

Stir-Fry Turkey

Prep time: 10 minutes

Cooking time: 5 minutes

Servings: 4

NUTRIENTS PER SERVING:

Carbohydrates – 42 g

Fat – 12 g

Protein – 29 g

Calories – 403

INGREDIENTS:

- 1 lb. turkey breast, cut into bite-sized pieces
- 1 tbsp avocado oil, or olive oil
- sea salt and black pepper to taste
- 1 large red pepper, sliced
- 1 cup mushrooms
- 1 cup zucchini, quartered
- 1 medium red onion, sliced

For the sauce:

- ¼ cup Bragg's liquid aminos
- ¼ cup soy sauce
- 1 tbsp raw honey
- 2 cloves fresh garlic, grated
- 1" fresh knob ginger, peeled and grated
- 1 tbsp sesame seeds

INSTRUCTIONS:

1. Mix the ingredients for the sauce in a bowl.
2. Heat the oil in a wok over a medium-high heat.
3. Add the turkey. Cook for 6-7 minutes.
4. Add all of the vegetables. Cook for 3-4 minutes.
5. Pour the sauce into the wok.
6. Stir well to coat the meat and vegetables.
7. Cook for 2-3 minutes.
8. Turn off the heat. Let it cool down.
9. Divide evenly between 4 containers.
10. Store in the fridge for 4-5 days. Enjoy!

Pesto Chicken and Vegetables

Prep time: 10 minutes

Cooking time: 15 minutes

Servings: 4

NUTRIENTS PER SERVING:

Carbohydrates – 15 g

Fat – 24 g

Protein – 22 g

Calories – 350

INGREDIENTS:

- 2 tbsp olive oil
- 4 boneless, skinless chicken thighs, sliced
- Salt to taste
- Pepper to taste
- 1 lb. green beans
- 2 cups cherry tomato, halved
- ½ cup basil pesto

7/1/22   PREP = Very Easy

TASTE =   8/10

Better than expected ☺

INSTRUCTIONS:

1. Heat the oil in a large pan.
2. Add and season the chicken thighs.
3. Cook until the meat is done.
4. Slice into strips and set aside.
5. Add the green beans. Cook to make them crisp-tender.
6. Put the chicken back into the pan, add the tomatoes and pesto, and stir well.
7. Divide all of the ingredients into 4 airtight containers.
8. Cover. Store in the fridge for 3-4 days.
9. Enjoy!

MEAT

Pork Chops with Green Beans and Potatoes

Prep time: 20 minutes

Cooking time: 1 hour 20 minutes

Servings: 5

NUTRIENTS PER SERVING:

Carbohydrates – 27 g

Fat – 8 g

Protein – 28 g

Calories – 307

INGREDIENTS:

- 2 lbs. pork sirloin chops
- 1 lb. red potatoes, halved
- 1 tsp olive oil
- 8 cups green beans
- Garlic to taste
- Salt to taste
- Pepper to taste

INSTRUCTIONS:

1. Preheat the oven to 400°F.
2. Line a baking sheet with parchment paper.
3. Spray with cooking oil.
4. Arrange the potatoes over the pan.
5. Spray with oil. Add salt and pepper.
6. Cover with foil. Bake for 30 minutes.
7. Remove the foil. Bake for 10-15 minutes more.

8. Take out and set aside.
9. Meanwhile, season each side of the pork chops with garlic, salt, and pepper.
10. Preheat the grill heat to high.
11. Sear each side of chops for 2-5 minutes.
12. Cook until the internal temperature of the meat reaches 160 degrees.
13. Heat 1 tsp of oil in a skillet over a medium heat.
14. Add the green beans. Cook for 10 minutes.
15. Divide all of the ingredients into 5 air-tight containers.
16. Cover and store in the fridge for 4-5 days. Enjoy!

Chipotle Beef

Prep time: 10 minutes
Cooking time: 8 hours
Servings: 10

NUTRIENTS PER SERVING:

Carbohydrates – 31 g
Fat – 13 g
Protein – 26 g
Calories – 345

INGREDIENTS:

- 1 tsp canola oil
- 1 small onion, chopped
- 1 can diced tomatoes,
- ¼ cup cider vinegar
- ¼ cup chopped chipotle peppers in adobo sauce + 2 tsp sauce
- 6 garlic cloves, minced
- 2 tbsp brown sugar
- 2 bay leaves
- ½ tsp ground cumin
- ½ tsp paprika
- ½ tsp pepper
- ¼ tsp ground cinnamon
- 1 boneless beef chuck roast
- 5 cups rice, cooked
- 4 cups cooked cauliflower rice
- 4 cups romaine lettuce
- 1 cup salsa
- 1 inch of cilantro, chopped
- lime wedges

INSTRUCTIONS:

1. Heat oil over medium-high.

2. Add onion. Cook for 2-3 minutes.
3. Add tomatoes, vinegar, peppers with sauce, garlic, brown sugar, bay leaves, and spices. Let it boil.
4. Reduce heat and simmer for 4-6 minutes.
5. Put roast and tomato mixture in a slow cooker. Cover the lid.
6. Set to 9 hours of low pressure.
7. Remove bay leaves and take out the roast.
8. Skim fat and shred beef, using forks.
9. Let all the ingredients cool down.
10. Divide and place all the ingredients in 5 air-tight containers.
11. Cover and store in the fridge for 4-5 days.
12. Enjoy!

Pork Green Chili

Prep time: 15 minutes

Cooking time: 6 hours

Servings: 5

NUTRIENTS PER SERVING:

Carbohydrates – 79 g

Fat – 28 g

Protein – 42 g

Calories – 676

INGREDIENTS:

- 6 pounds pork shoulder, trimmed and diced
- 2 yellow onions, chopped
- 8 cloves garlic, minced
- 1 tsp salt
- pepper to taste
- 24 ounces salsa verde
- 8 ounces canned green chilis
- 2 jalapeño peppers, chopped
- 1 small bunch cilantro, chopped
- 1 cup green onion, chopped
- 2 cans black beans
- 2 cans sweet corn, drained
- 5 cups fresh lettuce
- 1 red onion, diced
- 1 lime, sliced into wedges

INSTRUCTIONS:

1. Add pork, onion, garlic, salt, and pepper to your slow cooker.
2. Add salsa verde, green chilis, jalapeño peppers.

3. Lock the lid. Set to 5 hours of high pressure.
4. Add cilantro, green onion. Mix well.
5. Preheat oven to 400°F.
6. Line parchment paper in a large baking sheet with. Set aside.
7. Season potatoes with olive oil, salt, and pepper in a bowl and toss to coat.
8. Arrange sweet potatoes in one layer.
9. Bake for 20-25 minutes.
10. Let all the ingredients cool down.
11. Divide and place all the ingredients in 5 air-tight containers.
12. Cover and store in the fridge for 4-5 days. Enjoy!

Prep - recipe unclear
time consuming

taste 8/10

63

Steak and Potatoes

Prep time: 10 minutes

Cooking time: 2 hours

Servings: 4

NUTRIENTS PER SERVING:

Carbohydrates – 41 g

Fat – 19 g

Protein – 27 g

Calories – 420

INGREDIENTS:

- 1 lb. flank steak
- 4 medium red potatoes, diced
- 8 eggs
- 3 stalks broccoli
- 1 tbsp preferred seasoning

INSTRUCTIONS:

1. Put the flank steak into the slow cooker.
2. Season with your preferred spices.
3. Set to 2 hours on high.
4. After 30-40 minutes when the steak is done, add the diced potatoes to the meat.
5. Cook the potatoes until they are soft.
6. Meanwhile, cook the scrambled eggs.
7. Steam and season the broccoli.
8. Cut the steak into cubes.
9. Let all the ingredients cool down.
10. Divide all of the ingredients into 5 air-tight containers.
11. Cover and store in the fridge for 4-5 days.
12. Enjoy!

Pork Chops with Apples

Prep time: 5 minutes

Cooking time: 45 minutes

Servings: 4

NUTRIENTS PER SERVING:

Carbohydrates – 3 g

Fat – 16 g

Protein – 29 g

Calories – 455

INGREDIENTS:

- 2 tbsp ghee
- ½ tsp sea salt
- 4 pork chops, boneless
- 2 chayote, chopped to ½-inch chunks
- 2 tbsp monkfruit
- 1 tsp cinnamon
- ⅛ tsp nutmeg
- 1 tbsp apple cider vinegar

INSTRUCTIONS:

1. Melt the ghee over a medium heat.
2. Add the pork chops. Cook for 5 minutes.
3. Flip the chops. Add the chayote, sweetener, cinnamon, and nutmeg.
4. Pour the apple cider vinegar over the top.

5. Cook until the internal temperature of the meat reaches 160 degrees. Set aside.
6. Let the chayote mixture boil for 4-5 minutes. Reduce to a medium-low heat.
7. Cover and simmer for 40 minutes, stirring from time to time. Allow to cool when it's done.
8. Divide all of the ingredients into 5 air-tight containers.
9. Cover and store in the fridge for 4-5 days.
10. Enjoy!

Sriracha Meatballs

Prep time: 10 minutes

Cooking time: 2 hours

Servings: 8

NUTRIENTS PER SERVING:

Carbohydrates – 19 g

Fat – 11 g

Protein – 27 g

Calories – 295

INGREDIENTS:

- 1 2-lb. lean ground turkey
- 1 cup whole-wheat panko breadcrumbs
- 2 eggs
- ¼ cup green onions, chopped
- ½ tsp garlic powder
- ½ tsp salt
- ½ tsp black pepper

For the sauce:

- ¼ cup Sriracha
- 3 tbsp reduced-sodium soy sauce
- 3 tbsp rice vinegar
- 3 tbsp honey
- 1 tbsp grated fresh ginger
- 3 cloves garlic, minced
- ½ tsp toasted sesame oil

INSTRUCTIONS:

1. Preheat the oven to 375°F.
2. Line a large baking sheet with parchment paper. Set aside.

3. Combine the turkey, breadcrumbs, eggs, green onions, garlic powder salt, and pepper in a bowl.
4. Make 1½-inch balls and transfer them to baking sheets.
5. Bake for 20-25 minutes.
6. Meanwhile, mix the sauce ingredients in a saucepan.
7. Let it boil over a medium heat, stirring.
8. Then simmer for 10 minutes over a low heat.
9. Add the meatballs and toss to cover with sauce.
10. Divide all of the ingredients into 5 air-tight containers.
11. Cover and store in the fridge for 4-5 days. Enjoy!

prep easy

taste - spicy! 7/10.

Beef and Broccoli

Prep time: 15 minutes

Cooking time: 20 minutes

Servings: 4

NUTRIENTS PER SERVING:

Carbohydrates – 26 g

Fat – 16 g

Protein – 40 g

Calories – 398

INGREDIENTS:

- 1 sirloin steak, sliced
- 2 tsp cornflour
- 3 tsp baking soda
For the marinade:
- 150ml cold water
- 75ml light soy sauce
- 1 tsp sriracha sauce
- 3 garlic cloves, chopped
- 1-inch ginger, chopped
- 1 tsp honey
- 2 tbsp sesame seed oil
- 2 spring onions, sliced
For meal prep:
- 1 cup broccoli florets
- 2 cups rice, cooked
- 1 handful of green onion, sliced

INSTRUCTIONS:

1. Add the steak and soda to a bowl. Toss well.
2. Cover and put in the fridge for 5

minutes.
3. In another bowl, mix the cornflour with 3 tbsp of water to make a paste.
4. Add 100 ml cold water, soy sauce, Sriracha sauce, garlic, ginger, honey, and the spring onions.
5. Take the beef out and rinse to remove the soda.
6. Add to the bowl. Add 2 tsp cornflour.
7. Preheat the sesame oil in a sauté pan over a high heat.
8. Add the beef. Stir-fry for 3 minutes.
9. Pour the marinade over the meat.
10. Add the broccoli. Reduce the heat and cook for 6 minutes, stirring.
11. Let all the ingredients cool down.
12. Divide evenly between 4 containers
13. Store in the fridge for 4-5 days. Enjoy!

Skirt Steak

Prep time: 20 minutes

Cooking time: 40 minutes

Servings: 5

NUTRIENTS PER SERVING:

Carbohydrates – 52 g

Fat – 36 g

Protein – 53 g

Calories – 735

INGREDIENTS:

- 5 skirt steaks 8 ounces each
- 2 tsp ancho chili powder
- 1 tsp paprika
- ½ tsp ground coriander
- ½ tsp cayenne pepper
- 1 tsp light brown sugar
- 1 tsp dried thyme
- 2 tbsp veggie oil
- 2 cups green beans, cooked
- 2 cups mushrooms, cooked

INSTRUCTIONS:

1. Combine the ancho chili powder, paprika, coriander, cayenne pepper, sugar, thyme, and oil in a bowl.
2. Dry rub steaks and season with salt.
3. Let it sit for 20 minutes with the rub on.

4. Heat the oil in a pan over a medium-high heat.
5. Cook each side for 3 minutes without touching the steaks.
6. Transfer to a plate and cover with foil.
7. Let it rest for 5 minutes.
8. Cook the green beans and mushrooms in your preferred way.
9. Divide all of the ingredients into 4 air-tight containers.
10. Cover and store in the fridge for 4-5 days.
11. Enjoy!

SEAFOOD

Tuna and Sweet Potatoes

Prep time: 10 minutes

Cooking time: 20 minutes

Servings: 4

NUTRIENTS PER SERVING:

Carbohydrates – 33 g

Fat – 8 g

Protein – 38 g

Calories – 342

INGREDIENTS:

- 4 x 150g tuna steaks
- 1 tsp coarse sea salt
- 1 tbsp coconut oil, melted
- 2 tbsp pink peppercorns

For the sweet potatoes:

- 4 large sweet potatoes, cleaned
- 1 tbsp plain flour
- ½ tsp salt
- ½ tsp pepper
- ½ tbsp coconut oil, melted

INSTRUCTIONS:

1. Preheat the oven to 400°F.
2. Prick the potatoes all over with a fork.
3. Put the potatoes on a microwavable plate and cook on high for 5 minutes.
4. Let them cool and then cut into

   wedges.
5. Season the potatoes with flour, salt, pepper, and melted coconut oil and toss to coat.
6. Put then on a baking tray. Bake for 15-20 minutes.
7. Grease each side of the tuna steak with coconut oil, season with salt.
8. Preheat the oil in a pan and add the tuna steaks.
9. Cook each side for 3-4 minutes
10. Divide all of the ingredients into 4 air-tight containers.
11. Add your preferred greens as salad.
12. Cover. Store in the fridge for 4 days. Enjoy!

Lemon Roasted Salmon with Sweet Potato and Broccoli

Prep time: 10 minutes
Cooking time: 35 minutes
Servings: 3

NUTRIENTS PER SERVING:

Carbohydrates – 18 g
Fat – 15 g
Protein – 21 g
Calories – 282

INGREDIENTS:

- 2 medium sweet potatoes, cubed
- Sea salt + fresh black pepper
- ½ tsp cumin powder
- A few tbsp of olive oil
- 4 cups broccoli florets
- 12 ounces of wild-caught salmon filets
- 1 tbsp butter
- 2 tbsp lemon juice
- ¼ tsp garlic powder
- ⅛ tsp red pepper flakes

INSTRUCTIONS:

1. Preheat the oven to 425°F.
2. Put the potatoes on one sheet pan and the broccoli florets on another sheet pan.
3. Drizzle both with olive oil
4. Sprinkle the potatoes with salt, pepper, cumin. Toss well.
5. Toss the broccoli with the salt and pepper.
6. Bake the potatoes for 15 minutes. Set

broccoli aside.

7. Mix the butter, lemon juice, garlic powder, pepper flakes, thyme, salt and pepper in a bowl. Heat in the microwave to melt the butter.
8. Line a baking sheet with the foil and spray with oil.
9. Put the fillets on top and cover with the lemon sauce.
10. Take out the cooked potatoes and toss.
11. Put them back in the oven along with the broccoli florets and salmon for 12 minutes.
12. Divide all of the ingredients into 3 air-tight containers.
13. Add your preferred greens as salad.
14. Cover and store in the fridge for 3 days. Enjoy!

Garlic Shrimp and Veggies

Prep time: 10 minutes

Cooking time: 10 minutes

Servings: 4

NUTRIENTS PER SERVING:

Carbohydrates – 11 g

Fat – 14 g

Protein – 30 g

Calories – 228

INGREDIENTS:

- 3 tbsp ghee
- 1 tbsp olive oil
- 1 lb. large shrimp, tails off, peeled and deveined
- Salt to taste
- Black pepper to taste
- 1 tsp Italian seasoning
- 3 garlic clove, minced
- 2 big bell pepper, diced
- 1 medium red onion, chopped
- 2 medium zucchinis, chopped
- Fresh parsley for garnishing

INSTRUCTIONS:

1. Melt and heat the butter and oil in a large skillet over a medium high heat.
2. Add the shrimp. Sprinkle with salt, pepper and Italian seasoning. Cook for 3 minutes.
3. Add the garlic. Cook for 1 minute.
4. Set the shrimp aside.
5. Add the bell pepper, onions, zucchini, salt, and pepper. Cook for 3-5 minutes.
6. Put the shrimp back into the skillet. Mix well.
7. Divide all of the ingredients into 4 air-tight containers.
8. Add your preferred greens as a salad.
9. Cover. Store in the fridge for 4 days.
10. Enjoy!

Skillet Honey Lime Tilapia

Prep time: 1 hour

Cooking time: 10 minutes

Servings: 4

NUTRIENTS PER SERVING:

Carbohydrates – 1 g

Fat – 9 g

Protein – 20 g

Calories – 151

INGREDIENTS:

- 4 tilapia fillets
- Zest of 1 lime
- 2 tbsp lime juice
- 1 tbsp olive oil
- 1½ tbsp honey
- ½ tsp salt
- ½ tsp pepper
- 1 clove garlic, minced
- ½ cup whole wheat flour
- ¼ tsp salt
- ¼ tsp pepper
- 1-2 tbsp olive oil

INSTRUCTIONS:

1. Mix the lime juice and zest, olive oil, honey, salt, pepper, and garlic in a bowl.
2. Put the tilapia in a Ziploc bag and add the marinade to the bag.

3. Press the air out, seal it, and put it into the fridge for 1-4 hours.
4. Mix the flour, salt, and pepper in a shallow dish.
5. Preheat the oil in a skillet (medium heat).
6. Coat each tilapia fillet with the flour.
7. Cook each side of fillets for 3-5 minutes.
8. Divide all of the ingredients into 4 airtight containers.
9. Cover. Store in the fridge for 4 days.
10. Enjoy!

Shrimp Green Goddess Grain Bowl

Prep time: 20 minutes

Cooking time: 15 minutes

Servings: 4

NUTRIENTS PER SERVING:

Carbohydrates – 56 g

Fat – 14 g

Protein – 28 g

Calories – 433

INGREDIENTS:

- 1 clove garlic
- 2 green onions, chopped
- ⅓ cup fresh parsley leaves
- ⅓ cup fresh cilantro leaves
- ¼ cup lemon juice
- 2 tbsp olive oil
- ¼ tsp salt
- ¼ tsp pepper
- ½ avocado
- 2 tbsp plain Greek yogurt
- 2-4 tbsp water
- 1 lb. shrimp, peeled and deveined
- ¼ tsp red pepper flakes
- 1 tsp olive oil
- 3 cups cooked whole grain
- 3 cups baby greens of choice
- 1 cup broccoli florets, cooked and drained
- 1 cup spinach
- 1 cup frozen cooked edamame, thawed
- 1 cucumber, sliced

INSTRUCTIONS:

1. Add the garlic, green onions, parsley, cilantro, lemon juice, olive oil, salt, and pepper to the food processor and chop.
2. Remove 2 tbsp of the mixture. Set aside.
3. Add the avocado and yogurt to the food processor.
4. Pulse, adding water to reach the desired thickness.
5. Add the reserved herb mixture, pepper flakes and shrimp to a bowl and toss well.
6. Preheat the oil in a skillet over a medium heat.
7. Add the shrimp. Cook until they are done.
8. Divide all of the ingredients into 4 air-tight containers.
9. Cover. Store in the fridge for 4 days.
10. Enjoy!

Baked Lemon Cod

Prep time: 20 minutes

Cooking time: 15 minutes

Servings: 4

NUTRIENTS PER SERVING:

Carbohydrates – 6 g

Fat – 13 g

Protein – 41 g

Calories – 318

INGREDIENTS:

- 4 cod fillets- 5-6oz each
- 3 tbsp butter, melted
- 2 tbsp lemon juice
- 3 tbsp lemon zest
- ⅓ cup of flour
- 1½ tbsp of dill
- ¾ tsp of salt

INSTRUCTIONS:

1. Preheat the oven to 400°F.
2. Grease a baking sheet with spray.
3. Melt the butter and add it to a bowl. Add the lemon juice.
4. Mix the zest, flour, dill, and salt on a plate.
5. Dry the fillets with a paper towel.
6. Coat each fillet in the butter mixture.
7. Then coat each fillet in flour. Transfer to the baking sheet.
8. Bake until the fish is 145°F (12-15 minutes).
9. Divide all of the ingredients into 4 air-tight containers.
10. Cover. Store in the fridge for 4 days.
11. Enjoy!

Bang Bang Zucchini Noodles

Prep time: 10 minutes

Cooking time: 30 minutes

Servings: 4

NUTRIENTS PER SERVING:

Carbohydrates – 15 g

Fat – 8 g

Protein – 5 g

Calories – 185

INGREDIENTS:

- 4 medium zucchini, spiralized
- 1 tbsp olive oil
- 1 pound shrimp

For the sauce:

- ¼ cup + 2 tbsp Greek yogurt
- ¼ cup + 2 tbsp light mayonnaise
- ¼ cup + 2 tbsp Thai sweet chili sauce
- 1½ tbsp honey
- 1½ tsp sriracha sauce
- 2 tsp lime juice

INSTRUCTIONS:

1. Preheat the oil in a skillet over a medium-high heat.
2. Add the zucchini noodles. Let water release and fry until the zucchini noodles are cooked.

3. Drain the noodles. Allow to sit for 10 minutes.
4. Mix the sauce ingredients in a bowl.
5. Heat the oil in the skillet again.
6. Add the shrimp. Season to taste and cook until they are done.
7. Transfer the sauce into 4 sauce containers.
8. Mix the zucchini noodles and shrimp and let it cool.
9. Divide the ingredients evenly between 4 containers.
10. Store in the fridge for 3-4 days.
11. Enjoy!

Mango Cod

Prep time: 15 minutes

Cooking time: 15 minutes

Servings: 4

NUTRIENTS PER SERVING:

Carbohydrates – 60 g

Fat – 5 g

Protein – 28 g

Calories – 400

INGREDIENTS:

- 4 cod fillets 1 pound
- 4 cups white rice, cooked
- 2 bunches asparagus, steamed
- 2 tsp avocado oil, divided
- 1 small mango, diced
- 1 clove garlic, chopped
- 1.5 tbsp red onion, chopped
- 1 tbsp coconut aminos
- 1 tbsp fresh cilantro, chopped
- 1 lime, cut into wedge slices
- 1 lime juice
- ½ tsp pink Himalayan salt
- ½ tsp ground black pepper

INSTRUCTIONS:

1. Preheat the oven broiler and line a sheet pan with parchment paper.

2. Place the fillets on a sheet pan and coat with 1 tsp olive oil. Sprinkle with salt and pepper.
3. Place on the upper rack. Broil until cooked (10-12 minutes).
4. Heat a saucepan over a medium-high heat to prepare the mango relish.
5. Add 1 tsp oil, red onion, and garlic. Cook for 3 minutes.
6. Add the aminos, mango, and lime juice. Cook for 2 minutes, stirring.
7. Divide all of the ingredients into 4 air-tight containers.
8. Cover. Store in the fridge for 4 days.
9. Enjoy!

Salmon with Coconut Rice

Prep time: 10 minutes

Cooking time: 30 minutes

Servings: 3

NUTRIENTS PER SERVING:

Carbohydrates – 8 g

Fat – 15 g

Protein – 49 g

Calories – 390

INGREDIENTS:

For the salmon:
- 18 0z raw salmon fillets
- Pinch of sea salt & pepper
- ¾ cup bell pepper salsa

For the coconut rice:
- 1 tbsp minced garlic
- ⅓ cup red onion, diced
- 16 oz cauliflower pearls
- 3 oz water
- ½ lime juice
- 1 tbsp lime zest
- ½ cup full fat coconut milk
- ½ cup cilantro, chopped
- Salt and pepper to taste

INSTRUCTIONS:

1. Preheat a nonstick skillet over a medium-high heat. Spray with olive oil.
2. Add the garlic, red onion, and the cauliflower pearls/rice and mix together.
3. Add the water and lime juice. Mix well.
4. Cover and cook for 3-5 minutes.

5. Increase the heat of the skillet and add the zest and coconut milk. Mix well.
6. Let the cauliflower simmer for 7 minutes.
7. Add the cilantro and stir well. Set aside.
8. Season the salmon with salt and pepper.
9. Preheat a nonstick skillet over high heat.
10. Spray with olive oil. Put the salmon into the skillet. Sear each side for 3 minutes.
11. Divide all the ingredients into 3 air-tight containers.
12. Cover and store in the fridge for 3 days. Enjoy!

SIDE-DISHES

Kedgeree

Prep time: 10 minutes

Cooking time: 30 minutes

Servings:2

NUTRIENTS PER SERVING:

Carbohydrates – 19 g

Fat – 7 g

Protein – 74 g

Calories – 451

INGREDIENTS:

- 2 fillets smoked haddock
- 1 tsp Coconut Oil
- 1 white onion, chopped
- 1 tsp turmeric
- 1 tsp ground coriander
- 1 tsp medium curry powder
- 3 hard-boiled eggs, peeled and quartered
- 150g wholemeal rice, cooked
- 1 handful fresh coriander

INSTRUCTIONS:

1. Put the fillets into a frying pan over a medium heat. Pour in enough water to cover the fish.
2. Let it boil and reduce the heat.
3. Simmer for 5 minutes. When it's done, break into chunks and set aside.
4. Pour the water out and add the oil to the pan.
5. Add the onion. Simmer over a medium heat until golden.
6. Add the turmeric, coriander, and curry powder. Cook for 30 seconds, stirring.
7. Add the rice and haddock. Mix well.
8. Let all of the ingredients cool.
9. Divide all of the ingredients into 4 air-tight containers.
10. Cover. Store in the fridge for 4 days.
11. Enjoy!

Garlic Sweet Potato Fries

Prep time: 10 minutes

Cooking time: 30 minutes

Servings: 2

NUTRIENTS PER SERVING:

Carbohydrates – 34 g

Fat – 7 g

Protein – 3 g

Calories – 221

INGREDIENTS:

- 1 large sweet potato, to yield 3-4 cups
- 1 tbsp olive oil
- 1 garlic clove, minced
- 1 tsp salt, to taste
- 1 tbsp Italian parsley, chopped

INSTRUCTIONS:

1. Preheat the oven to 425°F.
2. Line a rimmed baking sheet with parchment paper. Set aside.
3. Mix the spices in a bowl.
4. Drizzle the sweet potatoes with olive oil, add the spices, and toss to coat.
5. Arrange the sweet potatoes in a single layer on the baking sheet.
6. Put on the lowest rack and bake for 15 minutes.
7. Then, flip the sweet potatoes using a spatula and bake for a further 15 minutes.
8. Let it cool when it's cooked.
9. Add to your meal prep dishes.
10. Enjoy!

Roasted Carrots

Prep time: 10 minutes

Cooking time: 20 minutes

Servings: 4

NUTRIENTS PER SERVING:

Carbohydrates – 1 g

Fat – 3 g

Protein – 1 g

Calories – 81

INGREDIENTS:

- 8 carrots, cut into 1-inch slices
- 1 tbsp olive oil
- ½ tsp paprika
- ⅛ tsp salt
- ⅛ tsp pepper

INSTRUCTIONS:

1. Preheat the oven to 425°F.
2. Arrange the carrots on a rimmed baking sheet.
3. Mix the oil, paprika, salt and pepper in a bowl.
4. Drizzle the carrots with the spice mixture and toss to coat.
5. Bake for 20 minutes.
6. Flip the carrots after 10 minutes using a spatula.
7. Add the cooked carrots to your meal prep.
8. Enjoy!

Stuffed Sweet Potato

Prep time: 20 minutes

Cooking time: 50 minutes

Servings: 4

NUTRIENTS PER SERVING:

Carbohydrates – 4 g

Fat – 5 g

Protein – 8 g

Calories – 93

INGREDIENTS:

- 4 medium sweet potatoes
- **For the Pepper Salsa:**
- 1 tbsp olive oil
- 1 cup diced colorful bell peppers
- 1 tbsp garlic, minced
- ½ can black beans, drained
- ⅓ cup frozen corn, thawed
- 4 Roma tomatoes. diced
- Sea salt & pepper to taste
- Spray olive oil
- **For the garnish:**
- 1 handful of cilantro, chopped
- Lime wedges
- 1 cup guacamole sauce

INSTRUCTIONS:

1. Preheat the oven to 420°F.
2. Make a few holes in the potatoes with a fork.

3. Put the potato on a baking sheet lined with parchment paper.
4. Wrap the potatoes in non-stick foil. Bake for 45 minutes.
5. Set a nonstick skillet to a medium heat.
6. Add the olive oil, bell peppers, and garlic. Cook for 3 minutes then add the black beans.
7. Add the corn and seasoning. Mix well and set aside.
8. Combine all of the ingredients and fill the potatoes with the pepper salsa.
9. Add the potatoes to your meal prep dishes. Enjoy!

Roasted Vegetable Grain Bowl with Tzatziki Sauce

Prep time: 10 minutes

Cooking time: 45 minutes

Servings: 4

NUTRIENTS PER SERVING:

Carbohydrates – 60 g

Fat – 10 g

Protein – 17 g

Calories – 399

INGREDIENTS:

- 3 cups cauliflower florets
- 1 red pepper, cubed
- 1 yellow pepper, cubed
- 1 red onion, cubed
- 1 zucchini, sliced
- 2 carrots, sliced
- 14 oz. can chickpeas
- 1½ tsp ground cumin
- 1 tsp smoked paprika
- 1 tsp garlic powder
- ½ tsp ground coriander
- ½ tsp ground cinnamon
- 2 tbsp olive oil
- **For Tzatziki Sauce:**
- ¾ cup plain greek yogurt
- ½ cup cucumber, grated
- 2 tbsp lemon juice
- 1 ½ tsp dry dill
- 1 garlic clove, grated
- 1 cup dry quinoa, cooked
- 2 cups water

INSTRUCTIONS:

1. Preheat the oven to 400°F.
2. Mix the cauliflower, red pepper, yellow pepper, red onion, zucchini, carrots, and chickpeas in one bowl.
3. Mix cumin, paprika, garlic powder, salt, cinnamon, coriander in another bowl.
4. Add the spice mixture and oil to the vegetables. Toss well.
5. Arrange the vegetables on a baking sheet.
6. Bake for 20 minutes. Flip the veggies with a spatula. Bake for another 10 minutes. Remove and set aside.
7. Mix the yogurt, cucumber, lemon juice, dry dill, garlic clove, and salt in a bowl.
8. Divide all of the ingredients into 4 airtight containers.
9. Cover. Store in the fridge for 4 days.
10. Enjoy!

Broccoli

Prep time: 5 minutes

Cooking time: 15 minutes

Servings: 3

NUTRIENTS PER SERVING:

Carbohydrates – 11 g

Fat – 6 g

Protein – 3 g

Calories – 55

INGREDIENTS:

- 1 head broccoli, chopped
- 2 cloves garlic, sliced
- 2 tbsp olive oil about
- 0.25 cup pine nuts
- 1 tbsp lemon juice
- ½ tsp salt

INSTRUCTIONS:

1. Preheat the oil in a pan over a high heat.
2. Add nuts and garlic. Cook until light brown.
3. Add all of the broccoli. Cook for 3 minutes over a high heat.
4. Put the cooked broccoli in a bowl and add the lemon juice and salt.
5. Mix well to combine.
6. Add the cooked broccoli to your meal prep dishes.
7. Enjoy!

Roasted Asparagus

Prep time: 5 minutes

Cooking time: 15 minutes

Servings: 3-4

NUTRIENTS PER SERVING:

Carbohydrates – 4 g

Fat – 3 g

Protein – 2 g

Calories – 96

INGREDIENTS:

- 1.5 lbs. asparagus spears, trimmed
- 2 cloves garlic, minced
- 1 tsp sea salt
- 3 tbsp extra virgin olive oil
- ½ tsp ground black pepper
- 1.5 tsp fresh lemon juice

INSTRUCTIONS:

1. Preheat the oven to 425°F.
2. Put the asparagus in a bowl.
3. Drizzle the asparagus with oil.
4. Sprinkle with salt, pepper, and garlic. Toss to coat.
5. Arrange the asparagus on a baking sheet in one layer.
6. Roast for 13-15 minutes.
7. Use for your meal prep.
8. Enjoy!

SALADS AND SNACKS

Protein Power Mason Jar

Prep time: 15 minutes

Cooking time: 15 minutes

Servings: 3

NUTRIENTS PER SERVING:

Carbohydrates – 10 g

Fat – 17 g

Protein – 27 g

Calories – 293

INGREDIENTS:

- 2 cups mixed greens
- 1 cup grape tomatoes, halved
- 1 cup pickling cucumber, quartered
- 1 carrot, shredded
- ½ cup quinoa
- 1 cup vegetable broth
- 1 can chickpeas, rinsed
- 1 can black beans

For the dressing:

- 3 tbsp avocado oil
- 1 tsp oregano
- Salt and pepper, to taste

INSTRUCTIONS:

1. Pour the vegetable broth into the pot and add the quinoa.
2. Cook on medium-low heat to absorb the liquid. Let it cool down.
3. Mix the avocado oil, oregano, salt, and pepper in a bowl.
4. Divide the dressing between the pre-prepared glass jars.
5. Assemble the jars with ingredients in this order: beans, chickpeas, quinoa, carrots, cucumbers, tomatoes, greens.
6. Cover and put in the fridge.
7. Store in the fridge for 2-3 days.
8. Enjoy!

Italian Couscous Salad

Prep time: 25 minutes

Cooking time: 25 minutes

Servings: 6

NUTRIENTS PER SERVING:

Carbohydrates – 51 g

Fat – 30 g

Protein – 20 g

Calories – 547

INGREDIENTS:

- 2 packages couscous, cooked
- 1 can chickpeas, drained
- 5 oz Genoa salami, chopped
- 5 oz Mozzarella Cheese, chopped
- 1 green bell pepper, chopped
- 5 oz black olives, sliced
- 2 cups cherry tomatoes, sliced
- ¾ cup fresh basil, chiffonade

For the dressing:

- ⅓ cup olive oil
- ⅓ cup red wine vinegar
- 1 tbsp Dijon mustard
- 1 tsp honey
- 1 tsp garlic, minced
- ½ tsp dried basil
- ½ tsp dried parsley
- ½ tsp dried oregano
- ¼ tsp red pepper flakes

INSTRUCTIONS:

1. Add the olive oil, mustard, honey, garlic, basil, parsley, oregano, pepper flakes, salt, and pepper to a glass jar. Mix well.
2. Divide the dressing evenly into 6 sauce containers.
3. Divide the vegetables evenly into 6 containers and put the sauce cups into each box.
4. Add the lemon wedges to each portion.
5. Cover and store in the fridge for 5-6 days. Enjoy!

Asian Chicken Mason Jar

Prep time: 5 minutes

Cooking time: 25 minutes

Servings: 4

NUTRIENTS PER SERVING:

Carbohydrates – 39 g

Fat – 33 g

Protein – 28 g

Calories – 524

INGREDIENTS:

- 1⅓ cup snap peas, halved
- 1 cup carrots, grated
- 1 red pepper, julienned
- 1⅓ cups cucumber, sliced
- 2 cups napa cabbage, sliced
- 2 cups baby spinach, sliced
- 2 cups rotisserie chicken, shredded
- 1 cup whole cashews
- 2 tbsp sliced green onions

For the sesame dressing:
- 3 tbsp low sodium soy sauce
- 2 tbsp rice vinegar
- 2 ½ tbsp toasted sesame oil
- 1 tbsp canola oil
- 1 tsp sriracha sauce
- 1 tbsp ginger, minced
- 1 garlic clove, minced
- 2 tbsp diced fresh cilantro
- 1 tbsp honey

- 1 tsp sesame seeds

INSTRUCTIONS:

1. Mix the soy sauce, rice vinegar, sesame oil, canola oil, sriracha sauce, ginger, garlic, cilantro, honey, and sesame seeds in a bowl.
2. Mix the cabbage and spinach in another bowl. Stir well to combine.
3. Divide all the ingredients evenly and assemble the jars in this order: dressing, snap peas, grated carrots, cucumbers, cabbage and spinach, rotisserie chicken, cashews.
4. Cover. Store in the fridge for 3-4 days.
5. Enjoy!

Full Harvest Quinoa Salad

Prep time: 10 minutes

Cooking time: 30 minutes

Servings: 2

NUTRIENTS PER SERVING:

Carbohydrates – 79 g

Fat – 36 g

Protein – 24 g

Calories – 707

INGREDIENTS:

- 2 cup sweet potato diced
- 1 tbsp olive oil
- Salt to taste
- Pepper to taste
- 2 cups cooked quinoa
- ½ cup pecans, chopped
- 4 cups raw spinach

For the dressing:

- 2 tbsp olive oil
- 2 tbsp apple cider vinegar
- 1 tbsp tahini
- 1 tsp miso
- ½ tsp garlic powder
- 1 pinch of sea salt
- Water to adjust the thickness

INSTRUCTIONS:

1. Preheat the oven to 425°F.
2. Put the sweet potatoes into a bowl.

3. Add the olive oil, salt and pepper. Toss to combine.
4. Arrange on a baking sheet. Bake for 30 minutes. Flip after 15 minutes with a spatula.
5. Let the potatoes cool down.
6. Mix the olive oil, apple vinegar, tahini, miso, garlic powder, and sea salt in a bowl to make the dressing.
7. Add 1 tbsp water to reach the desired thickness.
8. Assemble the mason jars with the ingredients in your preferred order.
9. Store in the fridge for 3-4 days. Enjoy!

Chicken, Apple and Pecan Salad

Prep time: 20 minutes

Cooking time: 10 minutes

Servings: 4

NUTRIENTS PER SERVING:

Carbohydrates – 40 g

Fat – 13 g

Protein – 24 g

Calories – 298

INGREDIENTS:

- 2 cups chopped kale leaves
- 2 Granny Smith apples, chopped
- ½ cup pecans, chopped
- 1 cup grapes

For the chicken salad:

- 2 boneless, skinless thin-sliced chicken breasts
- Kosher salt and black pepper, to taste
- ⅓ cup plain Greek yogurt
- ¼ cup red onion, diced
- 2 stalks celery, diced
- 2 tbsp mayonnaise, optional
- 2 tbsp almonds, sliced
- 1 tbsp lemon juice

INSTRUCTIONS:

1. Sprinkle the chicken breasts with salt and pepper.

2. Put chicken into the non-stick skillet.
3. Fry on each side until cooked through (3-4 minutes).
4. Let the chicken cool down and then dice.
5. Mix the chicken, greek yogurt, red onion, celery, mayonnaise, almonds, lemon juice, salt, and pepper in a bowl.
6. Divide all the ingredients evenly between 4 mason jars.
7. Cover. Store in the fridge for 3-4 days.
8. Enjoy!

Lemon Pepper Tuna-Salad

Prep time: 5 minutes

Cooking time: 28 minutes

Servings: 2

NUTRIENTS PER SERVING:

Carbohydrates – 1 g

Fat – 1 g

Protein – 18 g

Calories – 80

INGREDIENTS:

- 2 Bumble Bee Lemon & Pepper Seasoned Tuna Pouches
- 1 yellow bell pepper, diced
- 1 cup guacamole
- 1 handful of green onion, chopped
- 2 red apples, diced
- ½ cup red onion, diced

INSTRUCTIONS:

1. Assemble the mason jars with the salad ingredients in this order: dressing, apples, yellow bell pepper, red onion, lettuce, green onion.
2. Cover the jars and pack with tuna.
3. Store in the fridge for 2-3 days.
4. Serve with tuna on top.
5. Enjoy!

Turkey Cobb Salad

Prep time: 30 minutes

Cooking time: 30 minutes

Servings: 4

NUTRIENTS PER SERVING:

Carbohydrates – 14 g

Fat – 21 g

Protein – 27 g

Calories – 365

INGREDIENTS:

- 3 tbsp red wine vinegar
- 3 tbsp extra-virgin olive oil
- 2 tsp Dijon mustard
- ¼ tsp salt
- ¼ tsp ground pepper
- 8 cups romaine lettuce, chopped
- 2 scallions, sliced
- 1 cup cherry tomatoes, halved
- 3 ounces deli turkey, cubed
- 2 slices cooked bacon, cut
- 2 large hard-boiled eggs, halved
- ½ cup Cheddar cheese, shredded
- 1 avocado, sliced

INSTRUCTIONS:

1. Mix the vinegar, oil, mustard, salt, and pepper in a bowl to make the dressing.
2. Divide it between 4 glass jars.
3. Divide the rest of the ingredients between the jars.
4. Store in the fridge for 3-4 days.
5. Add sliced avocado and shredded cheese before serving.
6. Enjoy!

Hummus and Veggie Snack Box

Prep time: 10 minutes

Cooking time: 30 minutes

Servings: 4

NUTRIENTS PER SERVING:

Carbohydrates – 7 g

Fat – 6 g

Protein – 27 g

Calories – 198

INGREDIENTS:

- 2 cups hummus
- 4 red apples
- 4 carrots, quartered
- 4 cucumbers, quartered
- 1 cup almond nuts
- 200 g preferred cheese, sliced

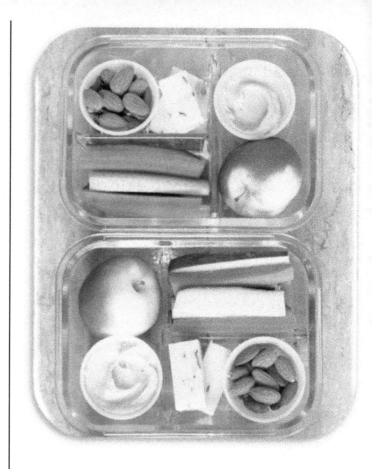

INSTRUCTIONS:

1. Cut all the ingredients and divide them evenly between 4 containers.
2. Put the hummus and almonds in small containers. Add to them to the veggies.
3. Cover. Store in the fridge for 3-4 days.
4. Enjoy!

VEGETARIAN AND VEGETABLE MEALS

Lentil Dal

Prep time: 10 minutes

Cooking time: 45 minutes

Servings: 3

NUTRIENTS PER SERVING:

Carbohydrates – 83 g

Fat – 6 g

Protein – 28 g

Calories – 504

INGREDIENTS:

- 1 tsp coconut oil
- 2 white onions, chopped
- 4 cloves garlic, chopped
- ½ tsp turmeric,
- ½ tsp ground cumin
- 500 ml water
- 1 tbsp medium curry powder
- 200g puy lentils
- 1 tin chickpeas, drained
- 1 cup broccoli florets
- 1 tin chopped tomatoes
- 1 vegetable stock cube
- 1 tsp black pepper
- 200g basmati or long-grain rice, cooked

INSTRUCTIONS:

1. Melt the oil in a saucepan over a medium heat.
2. Add the onions. Cook for 3-4 minutes.
3. Add the chickpeas and broccoli. Brown for 3-4 minutes.
4. Add the garlic, turmeric and cumin.
5. Dissolve the stock cube in boiling water.
6. Pour the stock into the saucepan.
7. Add the tomatoes and stir well.
8. Add the lentils and pepper. Reduce to a low heat.
9. Cover and cook for 30-35 minutes.
10. Let the lentils cool.
11. Divide evenly between 3 containers with the cooked rice.
12. Store in the fridge for 3 days. Enjoy!

Quinoa Burrito Bowls

Prep time: 15 minutes

Cooking time: 15 minutes

Servings: 5

NUTRIENTS PER SERVING:

Carbohydrates – 57 g

Fat – 20 g

Protein – 14 g

Calories – 445

INGREDIENTS:

- 3 cups quinoa, cooked
- 1 can black beans, drained & rinsed
- 1 red onion, diced
- 1 tsp cumin
- ½ tsp salt
- Juice of 1 lime
- 2 heads of romaine, chopped
- ½ cup salsa, divided
- 3 avocados, sliced
- Lime slivers optional

INSTRUCTIONS:

1. Mix the quinoa, beans, corn, cilantro, spices, and lime juice in a large bowl.
2. Stir well to combine.
3. Divide evenly and add 2 cups romaine, 1 ½ cups quinoa mixture, 1 tbsp salsa, and avocado slices to 5 containers.
4. Cover and store in the fridge for 4-5 days.
5. Enjoy!

Southwest Sweet Potato

Prep time: 15 minutes

Cooking time: 25 minutes

Servings: 4

NUTRIENTS PER SERVING:

Carbohydrates – 25 g

Fat – 1 g

Protein – 2 g

Calories – 110

INGREDIENTS:

- 1 sweet potato, diced
- 3-4 tbsp olive oil, divided
- 1 tsp southwest seasoning
- Garlic powder to taste
- Salt and pepper to taste
- 1 can sweet corn, drained
- 1 can black beans, drained and rinsed
- ½ tsp ground cumin
- ½ lime juice

INSTRUCTIONS:

1. Preheat the oven to 400°F.
2. Arrange the potato on a foil-lined baking sheet.
3. Add the southwest seasoning, garlic powder, salt, pepper, and olive oil. Toss to coat.
4. Bake for 25 minutes.
5. Mix the corn, beans, lime juice, 1 tbsp of olive oil, cumin, salt, and pepper in a bowl.
6. Let the potatoes cool down.
7. Divide the potatoes and corn-bean mixture evenly between 4 containers.
8. Store in the fridge for 5 days.
9. Enjoy!

Roasted Vegetable Quinoa Bowl

Prep time: 15 minutes

Cooking time: 25 minutes

Servings: 4

NUTRIENTS PER SERVING:

Carbohydrates – 23 g

Fat – 5 g

Protein – 5 g

Calories – 151

INGREDIENTS:

- 2-3 tbsp oil
- 1 tsp turmeric
- 2 medium-size sweet potatoes, diced
- 1 tsp chili powder
- 1 tsp cumin
- 1-pound brussels sprouts, halved
- 1 cup dry quinoa, rinsed and cooked
- 2 avocados for serving
- ½ cup tahini
- Juice of 1-2 lemons
- 2 tsp pure maple syrup
- Salt & pepper, to taste

INSTRUCTIONS:

1. Preheat the oven to 400°F.
2. Line two baking sheets with parchment paper.

3. Mix the sweet potato, 1 tbsp oil, chili powder, and cumin in a bowl. Toss and arrange on the baking sheet.
4. Put the brussels sprouts and oil in a bowl. Toss to coat with oil. Arrange on the baking sheet. Bake for 25 minutes.
5. Mix the tahini, juice of 1-2 lemons and maple syrup together. Add water to adjust the thickness.
6. Add the cooked vegetables to the quinoa and season with salt and pepper.
7. Store in the fridge for 3-4 days. Keep the tahini sauce and avocado separated. Enjoy!

Mediterranean Vegan Bowl

Prep time: 10 minutes

Cooking time: 20 minutes

Servings: 4

NUTRIENTS PER SERVING:

Carbohydrates – 60 g

Fat – 30 g

Protein – 18 g

Calories – 561

INGREDIENTS:

- ¾ cup cooked quinoa
- 1 can chickpeas, drained
- 2 cucumbers, diced
- Handful little tomatoes, halved
- 2 tbsp red onions, chopped
- Kalamata olives to taste
- Hummus to taste

INSTRUCTIONS:

1. Prepare and divide all of the ingredients evenly between 4 containers.
2. Put the hummus into separate mini sauce containers.
3. Store in the fridge for 3-4 days.
4. Enjoy!

Vegetarian Veggie Bowls

Prep time: 15 minutes

Cooking time: 45 minutes

Servings: 6

NUTRIENTS PER SERVING:

Carbohydrates – 40 g

Fat – 16 g

Protein – 25 g

Calories – 422

INGREDIENTS:

- 32 oz. frozen southern style
- 12 large eggs
- 15 oz. can black beans, drained and rinsed
- ¾ cup green onion, chopped
- ½ cup cilantro, chopped
- 6 oz. Mexican shredded cheese
- Salt and pepper to taste
- Taco sauce for serving, to taste

INSTRUCTIONS:

1. Preheat the oven to 375°F.
2. Line a baking sheet with parchment paper.
3. Arrange the frozen hash browns on the sheet.
4. Sprinkle with salt and pepper.
5. Bake for 45 minutes.
6. Whisk the eggs and season salt and pepper.
7. Cook the scrambled eggs the way you like them.
8. Add the greens to the cooked potatoes. Toss to coat. Let it cool.
9. Divide all of the ingredients evenly between 4 containers.
10. Cover and store in the fridge for 3 days.
11. Enjoy!

Power Up Bowl

Prep time: 10 minutes

Cooking time: 40 minutes

Servings: 4

NUTRIENTS PER SERVING:

Carbohydrates – 35g

Fat – 19 g

Protein – 16 g

Calories – 361

INGREDIENTS:

For the vegetables:

- 2 tbsp extra-virgin olive oil
- 1 small red onion, diced
- 2 sweet potatoes, diced
- 2 tsp chili powder, divided
- ¾ tsp salt, divided
- ¾ tsp black pepper, divided
- 1 cup broccoli and cauliflower florets

For the dressing:

- 3 tbsp lemon juice
- 3 tbsp tahini
- 1 clove garlic, minced
- ½-1 tsp ground cumin
- ¼ tsp kosher salt
- 4 hard-boiled eggs

INSTRUCTIONS:

1. Preheat the oven to 400°F.
2. Spray a baking sheet with oil spray.
3. Arrange the onion and potatoes on the sheet.
4. Drizzle with olive oil, 1 tsp chili powder, ¼ tsp salt, ¼ tsp pepper. Toss

to coat.

5. Bake for 10 minutes.
6. Take out the sheet from the oven and flip the sweet potatoes.
7. Push the potatoes to one side. Add the cauliflower and broccoli florets to the other side.
8. Season the florets with the rest of the olive oil, salt, pepper, and chili powder. Toss to coat.
9. Put the tray back into the oven. Bake for 25 minutes.
10. Meanwhile, mix the lemon juice, tahini, garlic, cumin, 2 tbsp hot water, and salt in a bowl.
11. Let the vegetables cool.
12. Divide the veggies and dressing between 4 containers.
13. Store in the fridge for 3-4 days. Enjoy!

DESSERTS

Peanut Butter Banana Splits

Prep time: 5 minutes

Cooking time: 15 minutes

Servings: 3

NUTRIENTS PER SERVING:

Carbohydrates – 49 g

Fat – 10 g

Protein –11 g

Calories – 317

INGREDIENTS:

- 3 bananas, sliced
- 1 tbsp coconut oil
- ½ cup chocolate chips
- 2 tbsp peanut butter
- Non-dairy whipped topping
- Maraschino cherries

INSTRUCTIONS:

1. Mix the chocolate chips, peanut butter, and coconut oil in a glass measuring cup.
2. Melt for 45-60 seconds. Stir it.
3. If it's not fully melted, melt for 5-10 more seconds.
4. Put the banana slices into 3 mason jars.
5. Pour the chocolate sauce over the bananas in each jar.
6. Put into the fridge and let it sit for 15 minutes.
7. Take the jars out of the freezer and top with non-dairy whipped topping, maraschino cherries, and chocolate sauce.
8. Store in the fridge for 2-3 days. Enjoy!

Chocolate Peanut Butter Chia Pudding

Prep time: 20 minutes

Cooking time: 20 minutes

Servings: 2

NUTRIENTS PER SERVING:

Carbohydrates – 18 g

Fat – 20 g

Protein – 11 g

Calories – 301

INGREDIENTS:

For the peanut butter layer:

- 1 cup almond milk
- 3 tbsp peanut butter
- 1-2 tbsp maple syrup to taste
- ¼ cup chia seeds
- ⅛ tsp kosher salt

For the chocolate layer:

- 1 cup almond milk
- 2 tbsp cocoa powder
- 1 tbsp peanut butter
- 2-3 tbsp maple syrup
- ¼ cup chia seeds
- ⅛ tsp kosher salt

INSTRUCTIONS:

1. Mix all of the ingredients for the peanut butter layer in a bowl.
2. Let it gel for 10 minutes.
3. Transfer the butter to a blender. Blend until smooth. Set aside.
4. Repeat steps 1-3 for the chocolate layer.
5. Layer the chocolate and peanut butter puddings in glass jars.
6. Store in the fridge for 1-2 days.
7. Enjoy!

Protein Rice Pudding

Prep time: 5 minutes

Cooking time: 30 minutes

Servings: 4

NUTRIENTS PER SERVING:

Carbohydrates – 38 g

Fat – 8 g

Protein – 32 g

Calories – 396

INGREDIENTS:

- 2 cups unsweetened almond milk
- 1 ¼ cup water
- 1 cup white rice
- 1 tsp ground cinnamon
- ⅓ cup coconut milk
- ¼ cup stevia sweetener
- 2 scoops vanilla protein powder
- ¼ cup almond milk

INSTRUCTIONS:

1. Add the almond milk, water, rice, vanilla, and cinnamon to a large pot. Cover with a lid.
2. Cook for 20 minutes over a medium-low heat.
3. Combine the vanilla protein powder, and 4 oz almond milk in a protein shaker bottle.
4. Shake to mix. Pour into the pot.
5. Add the coconut milk and stevia to the pot.
6. Mix all of the ingredients together.
7. Divide the pudding evenly into 4 containers.
8. Store in the fridge for 3-4 days.
9. Enjoy!

Cinnamon Roll Coffee Cake

Prep time: 15 minutes

Cooking time: 35 minutes

Servings: 12

NUTRIENTS PER SERVING:

Carbohydrates – 46 g

Fat – 21 g

Protein – 5 g

Calories – 377

INGREDIENTS:

- 12 eggs lightly beaten
- ¼ cup coconut oil, melted
- 1 cup coffee, cooled
- ½ cup milk
- 3 cups gluten-free all-purpose baking flour
- 1 cup unrefined coconut sugar
- 1 tbsp. baking powder

For the cinnamon swirl:

- ½ cup coconut oil
- ½ cup unrefined coconut sugar
- 2 tsp cinnamon
- 1 tbsp gluten-free flour

For the coconut glaze:

- ¼ cup coconut butter, softened
- 1 tsp unrefined coconut sugar

INSTRUCTIONS:

1. Preheat the oven to 350°F.
2. Grease a baking dish (9 x 13).
3. Combine the eggs, milk, coconut oil, cooled coffee, coconut sugar, flour, and baking powder. Mix well to make thick and sticky.
4. Pour the batter into the greased baking dish.
5. Mix the coconut oil, unrefined coconut sugar, flour, and cinnamon in a bowl until fluffy.
6. Spread the batter evenly in a baking dish.
7. Bake for 30-40 minutes.
8. Take the cake out of the oven.
9. Mix the ingredients for the coconut glaze together and cover the cake with it.
10. Let the cake cool. Cut it.
11. Divide between the meal prep containers.
12. Store in the fridge or 4-5 days. Enjoy!

Berry Almond Chia Pudding

Prep time: 5 minutes

Cooking time: 10 minutes

Servings: 3

NUTRIENTS PER SERVING:

Carbohydrates – 29 g

Fat – 11 g

Protein – 9 g

Calories – 252

INGREDIENTS:

- 1 tbsp. chia seeds
- 1-2 cups unsweetened almond milk
- 3 cups berries of choice
- Sweetener, if desired
- 1 pinch salt

INSTRUCTIONS:

1. Add the chia seeds, sweetener, salt, and almond milk to the bowl.
2. Mix well to combine. Cover with a lid.
3. Put into the fridge and let it sit overnight.
4. Take out of the fridge.
5. Divide the chia pudding and between 3 mason jars.
6. Store in the fridge for 4-5 days.
7. Enjoy!

Strawberry Cheesecake

Prep time: 4 hours

Cooking time: 30 minutes

Servings: 4

NUTRIENTS PER SERVING:

Carbohydrates – 9 g

Fat – 0 g

Protein – 9 g

Calories – 80

INGREDIENTS:

- 2 cups 2% plain greek yogurt
- ⅔ cup white sugar
- 1 tsp vanilla bean paste
- 2 large egg
- 3 tsp of cornstarch

For the strawberry topping:

- 4 cups strawberries, sliced
- Splash of water
- Drizzle of honey
- Extra yogurt, for garnish

INSTRUCTIONS:

1. Preheat the oven to 375°F.
2. Place two jars into a baking dish.
3. Add some water, so it comes up the sides of the jars about 1″. Set aside.
4. Add the yogurt, sugar, egg, cornstarch, and vanilla to the food processor. Blend well.

5. Divide the mixture between the jars and
6. bake for 23-26 minutes.
7. Cover the jars and chill in the fridge for at least 4 hours.
8. Mix the sliced strawberries + splash of water in a saucepan.
9. Cook over a medium heat for 5 minutes.
10. Turn off the heat. Add the honey.
11. Let the sauce cool. Cover the top of the cheesecakes in the jars with it.
12. Store in the fridge for 3-4 days. Enjoy!

DRINKS

Green Monster Smoothie

Prep time: 2 minutes

Cooking time: 10 minutes

Servings: 4

NUTRIENTS PER SERVING:

Carbohydrates – 36 g

Fat – 2 g

Protein – 6 g

Calories – 179

INGREDIENTS:

- ¼ cup blueberries
- ⅓ cup pineapple cubes
- ½ cup packed spinach
- ½ cup packed baby kale
- 1 tsp chia seeds
- 1 banana
- ¾ cup milk of choice

INSTRUCTIONS:

1. Add all of the ingredients (except milk) to a ziplock.
2. Remove all of the air from the bag.
3. Put in the freezer until you need it.
4. Add all of the contents of the pack to the blender.
5. Pour in ¾ cup of your choice of milk.
6. Enjoy!

Detox Smoothie

Prep time: 10 minutes

Cooking time: 10 minutes

Servings: 2

NUTRIENTS PER SERVING:

Carbohydrates – 47 g

Fat – 1 g

Protein – 4 g

Calories – 202

INGREDIENTS:

- 1 cup blueberries
- 1 cup spinach
- 1 tsp grated gingers
- ½ cup grapefruit, peeled
- ½ cup pineapple chunks
- 1 tbsp chia seed
- 3 frozen coconut milk ice cubes
- 1 scoop Collagen Protein

INSTRUCTIONS:

1. Freeze ¼ cup coconut milk in ice trays.
2. When it's frozen, add the rest of the ingredients to Ziploc bags.
3. Put in the freezer until you need it.
4. Add all of ingredients to the blender to make a smoothie. Add water if needed.
5. Enjoy!

Energizing Smoothie

Prep time: 10 minutes

Cooking time: 10 minutes

Servings: 2

NUTRIENTS PER SERVING:

Carbohydrates – 50 g

Fat – 2 g

Protein – 10 g

Calories – 227

INGREDIENTS:

- 1 tbsp cocoa powder
- ½ cup almond milk
- 1 –2 servings protein
- 1 banana
- ¼ cup gluten-free oats
- 1–2 tbsp flaxseed

INSTRUCTIONS:

1. Combine the cocoa powder, milk, and collagen protein peptides in a bowl.
2. Pour the mixture into the ice tray and freeze.
3. Add the rest of the ingredients to Ziploc bags.
4. Freeze the Ziplocs.
5. Blend it all together when you want to make the smoothie.
6. Enjoy!

Beautify Smoothie

Prep time: 5 minutes

Cooking time: 20 minutes

Servings: 10

NUTRIENTS PER SERVING:

Carbohydrates – 41 g

Fat – 25 g

Protein – 28 g

Calories – 475

INGREDIENTS:

- 1 kiwi, peeled
- 1 cup raspberries
- ½ avocado, peeled
- 1 tbsp honey
- 2–3 frozen coconut milk cubes
- Lavender Lemon Beauty Collagen Protein

INSTRUCTIONS:

1. Pour ¼ cup of coconut milk into the ice trays. Freeze it.
2. Add the rest of ingredients to Ziploc bags.
3. Freeze it until you want a smoothie.
4. Add all of the ingredients to a blender with the collagen protein powder and honey.
5. Enjoy!

Berries Detox Smoothie

Prep time: 5 minutes

Cooking time: 2 minutes

Servings: 2

NUTRIENTS PER SERVING:

Carbohydrates – 47 g

Fat – 3 g

Protein – 13 g

Calories – 222

INGREDIENTS:

- 2 cups frozen mixed berries
- 1 medium banana
- 1 large apple, cored
- Juice of 1 lemon
- 3-4 inch chunk cucumber
- ½ cup Italian flat-leaf parsley
- 1 cup kale
- 1 tbsp chia seeds
- 1 cup coconut milk
- 1 cup water, more if needed

INSTRUCTIONS:

1. Put all of the ingredients into a blender.
2. Blend until all of the ingredients are smooth.
3. Add more water if needed.
4. Cover. Store in the fridge for 1-2 days.
5. Enjoy!

Kale Pineapple Smoothie

Prep time: 10 minutes

Cooking time: 10 minutes

Servings: 1

NUTRIENTS PER SERVING:

Carbohydrates – 27 g

Fat – 9 g

Protein – 8 g

Calories – 187

INGREDIENTS:

- ¼ cup pineapple, frozen
- 2 cup kale leaves, de-stemmed
- 1 tbsp coconut oil
- ½ avocado
- 1 cup coconut water
- 1 tsp matcha green tea
- ½ cup full fat plain Greek yogurt

INSTRUCTIONS:

1. Add all of the ingredients to a blender.
2. Blend to make the smoothie.
3. Pour in additional water if needed.
4. Cover. Store in the fridge for 1-2 days.
5. Enjoy!

Vanilla Protein Shake

Prep time: 10 minutes

Cooking time: 10 minutes

Servings: 1

NUTRIENTS PER SERVING:

Carbohydrates – 7 g

Fat – 5 g

Protein – 30 g

Calories – 208

INGREDIENTS:

- 1 cup almond milk
- 1 cup whey protein powder
- ⅓ cup vanilla Greek yogurt
- 1 tsp vanilla extract

INSTRUCTIONS:

1. Add the milk, protein powder, yogurt, and vanilla extract to a blender.
2. Blend well to make a smoothie.
3. Add more water if needed.
4. Cover. Store in the fridge for 1-2 days.
5. Enjoy!

CONCLUSION

Thank you for reading this book and having the patience to try the recipes.

I do hope that you have had as much enjoyment reading and experimenting with the meals as I have had writing the book.

Stay safe and healthy!

Recipe Index

Conversion Tables

VOLUME EQUIVALENTS (LIQUID)

US STANDARD	US STANDARD (OUNCES)	METRIC
2 tablespoons	1 fl. oz.	30 mL
¼ cup	2 fl. oz.	60 mL
½ cup	4 fl. oz.	120 mL
1 cup	8 fl. oz.	240mL
1½ cups	12 fl. oz.	355 mL
2 cups or 1 pint	16 fl. oz.	475 mL
4 cups or 1 quart	32 fl. oz.	1 L
1 gallon	128 fl. oz.	4 L

OVEN TEMPERATURES

FAHRENHEIT (°F)	CELSIUS (°C) APPROXIMATE
250 °F	120 °C
300 °F	150 °C
325 °F	165 °C
350 °F	180 °C
375 °F	190 °C
400 °F	200 °C
425 °F	220 °C
450 °F	230 °C

VOLUME EQUIVALENTS (LIQUID)

US STANDARD	METRIC (APPROXIMATE)
⅛ teaspoon	0.5 mL
¼ teaspoon	1 mL
½ teaspoon	2 mL
⅔ teaspoon	4 mL
1 teaspoon	5 mL
1 tablespoon	15 mL
¼ cup	59 mL
⅓ cup	79 mL
½ cup	118 mL
⅔ cup	156 mL
¾ cup	177 mL
1 cup	235 mL
2 cups or 1 pint	475 mL
3 cups	700 mL
4 cups or 1 quart	1 L
½ gallon	2 L
1 gallon	4 L

WEIGHT EQUIVALENTS

US STANDARD	METRIC (APPROXIMATE)
½ ounce	15 g
1 ounce	30 g
2 ounces	60 g
4 ounces	115 g
8 ounces	225 g
12 ounces	340 g
16 ounces or 1 pound	455 g